without the calories | easy one pot
Justine Pattison

For Damon

without the calories

easy one pot

Justine Pattison

Low-calorie recipes, cheats and
ideas for fuss-free meals

28 29 30 31 32 33 34 3/5

contents

introduction

MY STORY

I struggled with my weight for years. After being a skinny child and teenager, I piled on the weight during my last years of school and went into my twenties feeling fat and frumpy. A career as a cookery writer and food stylist has helped me understand good food but because my kitchen is always overflowing with great things to eat, temptation is never far away. My weight yo-yoed for twenty years and at my heaviest I weighed more than 15 stone.

A few years ago, I worked on the hit TV series *You Are What You Eat* – I put together those groaning tables of bad food. I also had the chance to work with the contributors on the show, guiding them through the dieting process and helping them discover a whole new way of eating and cooking. Having been overweight myself, I became passionate about helping people lose weight.

Since then, I've worked as a food consultant on many of the weight-loss shows you've seen on TV, and written diet plans and recipes for best-selling books, newspapers and magazines. I'm thrilled that thousands of people have successfully followed my way of cooking and lost weight.

This book, and the others in the *Without the Calories* series, are ideal for anyone who wants to lose weight while leading a normal life. Cooking my way will help you sustain a happy, healthy weight loss. That's what it's all about: you don't have to be stick thin, but you deserve to feel good about yourself. My *Without the Calories* recipes will help you reach your goal.

ABOUT THIS BOOK

When you are busy, finding time to shop and cook can be tough – and it's not just the preparation – by the time you've finished your meal, there could be a stack of washing up waiting to be done too.

In this book, I've minimised the work and cleaning up needed to create a host of easy, delicious and complete low-calorie meals. Most recipes only require one dish – whether it's a saucepan, wok, casserole or serving bowl. Sometimes a recipe will require a bowl or plate for mixing ingredients or measuring, for a dressing or sauce for instance, but I've kept the call for additional equipment as low as possible.

I've reworked the ingredients and used crafty cooking methods to reduce the calories while ensuring that every dish remains as delicious as possible. There are no complicated methods, just simple food cooked without fuss.

I'm not going to make rash promises about how many pounds you will shed, but I do know that when it comes to losing weight, finding foods that give you pleasure and fit into your lifestyle are the key to success. When you eat well without obsessing over rapid weight loss, it's easier to relax and lose what you need to comfortably – and safely.

To help everyone enjoy these reinvented dishes, I've used easy-to-find ingredients and given clear, simple cooking instructions. There's also freezer information included where appropriate, so you know which dishes you can store safely for another day.

If you're already following a diet plan, you'll find additional nutritional information at the back of the book that'll help you work my recipes into your week. And, if you're stuck for inspiration and have a few pounds to lose, try my 123 Plan. It couldn't be easier.

USING THE 123 PLAN

If you're not following a diet regime at the moment and want a great kick-start, try my 123 Plan for a few weeks. I've tried to make it really easy, and you don't need to do too much adding up. You will find over 500 recipes to choose from in the *Without the Calories* series. Just pick one breakfast or main meal recipe a day from each section to bring your daily intake to between 900 and 1,200 calories. Add an *essential extra* 300 calories a day from a choice of accompaniments, snacks or desserts, and you'll be on your way to a healthy, sustainable weight loss of between 2–3lbs a week.

ONE
up to 300 calories

TWO
300–400 calories

THREE
400–560 calories

YOUR ESSENTIAL EXTRAS

These extra 300 calories can be made up of accompaniments, such as potatoes, rice and pasta, as well as snacks or treats; there are suggestions and serving sizes on page 180. You'll also find recipes that contain under 200 calories per portion, which can be included as part of your essential extras. As long as your extras don't exceed 300 calories a day, you'll be on track.

WHEN TO EAT

The 123 Plan is flexible, so if you find you fancy a **ONE** or **TWO** recipe rather than a **THREE** as your third meal of the day, just add enough calories to bring it into the right range. Don't worry if the calculations aren't absolutely accurate – a difference of 25 or less calories per serving won't affect your weekly allowance.

If you want to add your own favourite meals into the plan, just make sure they are within the recommended calorie boundaries and calculate accordingly. (You may find this useful when planning breakfast especially.)

DON'T RUSH IT

Weight tends to be gained over time, and losing it gradually will make the process easier and help give your body, especially your skin, time to adapt. You're more likely to get into positive, enjoyable long-term cooking and eating habits this way too.

WHAT IS A CALORIE?

Put simply, a calorie is a unit of energy contained within food and drink which our bodies burn as fuel. Different foods contain varying amounts of calories and if more calories are consumed than the body needs, the excess will be stored as fat. To lose weight, we need to eat less or use more energy by increasing our activity – and ideally both!

I've provided the calorie content of a single serving of each dish. In my experience, most people will lose at least 2lb a week by consuming around 1,200–1,500 calories a day, but it's always best to check with your GP before you start a new regime. Everyone is different and, especially if you have several stones to lose, you'll need some personalised advice. The calories contained in each recipe have been calculated as accurately as possible, but could vary a little depending on your ingredients. If you have a couple of days of eating more than 1,400 calories, try to eat closer to 1,100 for the next few days. Over a week, things will even out.

My recipes strike a balance between eating and cooking well and reducing calories, and I've tried them all as part of my own way of enjoying food without putting on excess weight. Even if you don't need to lose weight, I hope you enjoy cooking from my books simply because you like the recipes.

SECRETS OF SUCCESS

The serving sizes that I've recommended form the basis of the nutritional information on page 182, and if you eat any more, you may find losing weight takes longer. If you're cooking for anyone who doesn't need to watch their calorie intake, you can increase their servings, but bear in mind that too much sugar isn't good for anyone.

The right portion size also holds the key to maintaining your weight loss. Use this opportunity to get used to smaller servings. Work out exactly how much food your body needs to maintain the shape that makes you feel great. That way, even when counting calories feels like a distant memory, you'll remain in control of your eating habits.

Stick to lean protein (which will help you feel fuller for longer) and vegetables and avoid high-fat, high-sugar snacks and confectionery. Be aware that alcohol is packed with empty calories and could weaken your resolve. Starchy carbs such as pasta, rice, potatoes and bread are kept to a minimum because I've found that, combined with eating lots of veg and good protein, this leads to more sustainable weight loss. There's no need to avoid dairy products such as cheese and cream, although they tend to be high in fat and calories. You can swap the high-fat versions for reduced-fat ones, or use less.

Ditch heavily processed foods and you will feel so much better. Switching to more natural ingredients will help your body work with you.

Most recipes in the *Without the Calories* series form the main part of each meal, so there's room to have your plate half-filled with freshly cooked vegetables or a colourful, crunchy salad. This will help fill you up, and boost your intake of vitamins and minerals.

Make sure you drink enough fluids, especially water – around 2 litres is ideal. Staying hydrated will help you lose weight more comfortably, and it's important when you exercise too.

IN THE KITCHEN

Pick up some electronic kitchen scales and a set of measuring spoons if you don't already have them. Both will probably cost less than a takeaway meal for two, and will help ensure good results.

Invest, if you can, in a large, deep non-stick frying pan, a medium non-stick saucepan and a large saucepan for pasta (so it can bubble freely). The non-stick coating means that you will need less oil to cook, and a frying pan with a wide base and deep sides can double as a wok. Non-stick baking parchment will prevent sticking and means you can use less oil. Look at the oven temperatures carefully. All the recipes in this book have been tested using a fan oven setting, which is always best for baking.

I use oil and butter sparingly, and use a mild olive oil spray for frying. I also keep a jam jar containing a little sunflower oil and a heatproof pastry brush to hand for greasing pans lightly before baking and frying.

STICK WITH IT

Shifting your eating habits and trying to lose weight is not easy, especially if you have been eating the same way for many years. But it isn't too late. You may never have the perfect body, but you can have one that, fuelled by really good food, makes you feel happy and healthy. For more information, tips and ideas, visit www.justinepattison.co.uk.

Justine

baking
tray

353
CALORIES
PER SERVING

quick cheesy
chicken and ham

SERVES 4
PREP: 10 MINUTES
COOK: 40 MINUTES

oil, for spraying or brushing
500g medium potatoes
    (ideally Maris Piper),
    peeled and cut into
    roughly 2.5cm chunks
4 boneless, skinless chicken
    breasts (each about 175g)
4 thin slices of Emmental
    or Gruyère cheese (each
    slice about 25g)
4 thin slices of prosciutto
    or serrano ham
250g bunch slender
    asparagus spears,
    trimmed and halved
flaked sea salt
ground black pepper

Tip: Use thin cheese slices
from a resealable pack for
stuffing the chicken. Freeze
any leftover cheese for up
to 1 month.

Cheese-filled chicken breasts wrapped in prosciutto and roasted with potatoes and asparagus. What's not to like?

Preheat the oven to 200°C/Fan 180°C/Gas 6. Spray or brush a large baking tray with oil, add the potatoes, spray with more oil and season with salt and pepper. Roast for 15 minutes.

While the potatoes are cooking, place one of the chicken breasts on a board with the smooth side underneath. Using a sharp knife, carefully cut horizontally through the breast from the curved side almost all the way through to the other side and open it out like a book. You may need to cut a little way, then gently flip the breast open and carry on gently cutting through the meat so it opens easily without tearing.

Place a slice of cheese over the open chicken breast and fold the chicken back over to completely enclose the cheese. Repeat with the other chicken breasts. Wrap each chicken breast in a slice of ham, to seal the cheese inside, season generously with salt and pepper and set aside.

Take the baking tray out of the oven and turn the potatoes. Nestle the chicken breasts among the potatoes, spray with a little oil and roast for 15 more minutes.

Take the baking tray out of the oven once more and dot the asparagus spears among the chicken and vegetables. Return to the oven for a further 10–12 minutes, or until the chicken is cooked through and the asparagus is just tender. Serve on warmed plates.

10 BAKING TRAY

461
CALORIES
PER SERVING

soda can roast chicken with chipotle mayonnaise

SERVES 4

PREP: 15 MINUTES

COOK: 1–1¼ HOURS

1 chicken (about 1.2kg)
330ml can Diet Coke
   or diet lemonade
800g medium potatoes
   (ideally Maris Piper),
   peeled and quartered
   into roughly 4cm chunks
oil, for spraying or brushing
2 bushy thyme sprigs,
   leaves stripped off
   (optional)
1–2 rosemary sprigs, leaves
   stripped off (optional)
flaked sea salt
ground black pepper
large mixed salad, to serve

FOR THE CHIPOTLE MAYO
75g reduced-fat
   mayonnaise
50g fat-free fromage frais
2 tsp chipotle paste
   (from a jar)
1 tsp fresh lemon juice
1 garlic clove, crushed
   or finely grated

Tip: Chipotle paste is made
from smoked jalapeño
peppers. It's available in
larger supermarkets but
you can substitute with
harissa paste, which will
give a different but just as
delicious flavour, or leave
it out altogether to make
a garlic mayo.

This is a fab way of roasting a chicken and it guarantees delicious roasted potatoes. If you stand the chicken on a can of fizzy Coke or lemonade, it stays moist, cooks more quickly and saves space in the roasting tin. If you have the chicken with skin the calories will increase to 539 per serving.

Preheat the oven to 200°C/Fan 180°C/Gas 6. Rearrange the shelves so you just have one shelf on the bottom rung, leaving space for the chicken to stand upright.

Untruss the chicken by removing the string. Season all over with salt and pepper. Open the can of Coke or lemonade and drink or pour away half of it. There should be enough left to hold the chicken steady when it sits on top of the can.

Put the potatoes in a large roasting tin and spray or brush with oil. Season well with salt and pepper and make a small gap in the centre. Set the can in the gap and ease the chicken on top of it.

Roast the chicken for 30 minutes, then take the roasting tin out of the oven very carefully and turn all the potatoes. Sprinkle with thyme and rosemary leaves, if using. Return to the oven for a further 30–45 minutes or until the chicken is thoroughly cooked and the potatoes are golden.

While the chicken is in the oven, mix all the ingredients for the chipotle mayo in a bowl.

Remove the roasting tin from the oven and very carefully lift the chicken off the can – you may need someone to hold the can with an oven glove while you lift the chicken. Discard the liquid inside the can. Put the chicken on a board and carve. Divide the chicken and potatoes between four warmed plates. Serve with a large salad and the chipotle mayo.

463
CALORIES
PER SERVING

all-in-one roast chicken dinner

SERVES 4
PREP: 20 MINUTES
COOK: 1 HOUR 10 MINUTES

500g medium potatoes (ideally Maris Piper), peeled and cut into roughly 4cm chunks

4 medium carrots (each about 100g), peeled and cut into 5cm long batons

2 medium parsnips (each about 150g), peeled and cut into 5cm long batons

oil, for spraying or brushing

40g dried sage and onion stuffing mix

8 boneless, skinless chicken thighs (about 675g), trimmed of visible fat

4 lean smoked back bacon rashers (about 125g), trimmed of visible fat and cut into 3cm slices

150g thin long-stemmed broccoli, trimmed and rinsed in cold water

2 tbsp Marsala or Madeira wine

250ml chicken stock (made with ½ chicken cube)

1 tbsp redcurrant jelly

flaked sea salt

ground black pepper

Tips: Use red or white wine instead of the Marsala for the gravy if you like, and add ½ teaspoon caster sugar.

Use kitchen scissors to remove the visible fat from the chicken.

A brilliant way to feed the family with hardly any washing up! The chicken pieces, all the vegetables and even the gravy is cooked in one tin. Use a roasting tin or baking tray with a good thick base as it will need to go on the hob to make the gravy. If your tray is a little flimsy, deglaze the pan with the stock to collect all the juicy bits, then make the gravy in a small saucepan. Sprinkling the chicken with stuffing mix adds a lovely herb flavour and a bit of crunch.

Preheat the oven to 200°C/Fan 180°C/Gas 6. Put the potatoes, carrots and parsnips in a large roasting tin or baking tray and spray or brush generously with the oil. Season with salt and pepper and roast for 25 minutes.

Put the stuffing mix in a sturdy freezer bag. Take the tin of vegetables out of the oven and turn them over.

Drop the chicken thighs one at a time into the bag with the stuffing mix and turn to coat. Place the thighs among the vegetables, arranging them into nice neat shapes. Spray or brush with more oil and bake for a further 25 minutes.

Take the roasting tin out of the oven and add the bacon slices and broccoli, nestling them among the chicken pieces and root vegetables. Spray with a little more oil. Return to the oven for a further 15 minutes or until the chicken is cooked through and lightly browned, and the vegetables are tender.

Transfer the contents of the roasting tin to a warmed platter or serving dish. Place the roasting tin on the hob and pour over the Marsala or Madeira and the stock. Add the redcurrant jelly and bring to a simmer. Cook for 2–3 minutes or until the liquid has reduced by half, stirring to scrape up the juicy bits from the bottom of the pan. Season to taste with salt and pepper then strain into a small warmed jug. Serve with the chicken and vegetables.

381

CALORIES
PER SERVING

barbecue-style chicken with potato wedges and corn

SERVES 4
PREP: 15 MINUTES
COOK: 40 MINUTES

1 tsp smoked paprika
1 tsp ground black pepper,
   plus extra to season
½ tsp fine sea salt,
   plus extra to season
8 boneless, skinless chicken
   thighs (about 675g),
   trimmed of visible fat
2 x 200g potatoes (ideally
   a floury variety such as
   King Edward or Maris
   Piper), washed, patted
   dry and each cut into
   10–12 long wedges
oil, for spraying or brushing
2 sweetcorn cobs
   (each about 250g)
1 tbsp cold water
10g butter
large mixed salad, to serve

FOR THE BARBECUE SAUCE
3 tbsp tomato ketchup
1½ tbsp clear honey
1 tbsp Worcestershire sauce

This is a dish that all the family will enjoy. The chicken pieces are deliciously sticky and sweet and the potatoes and corn can be conveniently baked in the oven alongside them. If you do have any chicken left over, it's great served with salad for lunch the next day.

Preheat the oven to 200°C/Fan 180°C/Gas 6. Line the base and sides of a large baking tray with a piece of foil (this will stop the sauce sticking and making the tray difficult to clean).

Put the paprika, pepper and salt in a large freezer bag. Carefully slash each chicken thigh 2–3 times with a sharp knife. Add the chicken to the bag with the seasoning and toss well until it is lightly coated. Place the chicken on the lined tray, arranging the thighs into nice neat shapes.

Place the potato wedges at one end of the same tray as the chicken and spray or brush with oil. Season with salt and pepper.

Cut the two sweetcorn cobs in half widthways and place them on a large square of foil. Bring up the sides and pour the cold water over the cobs. Add the butter and fold over the top tightly to make a sealed parcel.

Place the chicken and potatoes on the top shelf of the oven and put the foil parcel containing the sweetcorn on the shelf beneath. Bake for 30 minutes.

To make the barbecue sauce, mix the ingredients together in a bowl. Take the baking tray out of the oven, turn the potatoes and spoon the sauce liberally over the chicken. Return to the oven and cook for a further 10 minutes. Serve the chicken, wedges and corn with a large mixed salad.

361
CALORIES
PER SERVING

lemony chicken tray bake

SERVES 4
PREP: 15 MINUTES
COOK: 50-65 MINUTES

2 medium red onions,
   each cut into 8 wedges
500g potatoes (ideally
   Maris Piper), peeled
   and cut into roughly
   3cm chunks
4 large tomatoes, quartered
oil, for spraying
8 boneless, skinless chicken
   thighs (about 675g),
   trimmed of visible fat
1 large red pepper,
   deseeded and cut into
   roughly 3cm chunks
1 large yellow pepper,
   deseeded and cut into
   roughly 3cm chunks
½ tsp sweet smoked
   paprika
½ tsp dried oregano
1 large lemon, halved
   lengthways
flaked sea salt
ground black pepper
chopped flat-leaf parsley,
   to garnish (optional)

A light and summery dish of tender chicken thighs baked with lots of colourful vegetables and lemony roast potatoes. A little olive oil can be drizzled over the top, but you'll need to add around 80 calories for each tablespoon. Serve with a lightly dressed green salad, if you like.

Preheat the oven to 200°C/Fan 180°C/Gas 6. Put the onions, potatoes and tomatoes in a large roasting tin or scatter them over a large baking tray and season with salt and lots of freshly ground black pepper. Spray with oil and toss together lightly. Roast for 20 minutes.

While the vegetables are roasting, put the chicken thighs on a board. Carefully slash each thigh 2–3 times with a knife.

Take the roasting tin or baking tray out of the oven, add the pepper chunks and turn the vegetables a couple of times. Place the chicken in the tin or tray and season all over with black pepper. Mix the paprika and oregano together and sprinkle over the top. Thickly slice one half of the lemon and add to the tin. Squeeze the juice from the other half over the chicken and vegetables.

Return to the oven for a further 30–45 minutes, or until the vegetables are tender and lightly charred and the chicken is thoroughly cooked. Plate the chicken and vegetables and spoon over the lemony tomato cooking juices. Garnish with chopped parsley, if you like.

556

no-fuss roast lamb

SERVES 6
PREP: 20 MINUTES
COOK: 2½ HOURS,
PLUS RESTING TIME

1.5kg whole leg of lamb
800g medium potatoes
   (ideally Maris Piper)
500g medium-large carrots
500g medium-large
   parsnips
oil, for spraying or brushing
300g fine green beans,
   trimmed
flaked sea salt
ground black pepper

FOR THE GRAVY
2 tbsp plain flour
100ml red wine
500ml hot lamb stock
   (made with 1 lamb cube)
1 tbsp redcurrant jelly

Tip: Use a roasting tin or baking tray with a thick base as it will need to go on the hob to make the gravy. If your tray is a little flimsy, deglaze the pan with the stock to collect all the juicy bits, then make the gravy in a small saucepan.

I thought a lot about this recipe and was originally planning something quite fancy. In the end, however, I opted for the sort of meal my family like to eat regularly. There isn't anything unusual about this simple combination of ingredients, but it's easy to knock together and great for lunch on a busy Sunday.

Preheat the oven to 200°C/Fan 180°C/Gas 6. Place the lamb in a large, sturdy roasting tin and season well with salt and pepper. Roast for 1¼ hours.

While the lamb is roasting, prepare all the vegetables. Peel and quarter the potatoes and peel the carrots and parsnips and cut them into short batons, each about 4cm long and 1.5cm wide. Keeping them a similar size will help them cook more evenly and because they are small, they will cook quickly, too.

Take the lamb out of the oven and transfer it to a board. Place the vegetables into the tin and spray or brush with oil. Season with salt and pepper and toss well together. Place the lamb on top of the vegetables and return to the oven for a further hour.

Remove the tin from the oven and transfer the lamb to a board again. Loosely cover with foil and a couple of folded tea towels. Add the green beans to the roasting tin and turn the root vegetables and beans. Return to the oven for a further 10 minutes or until the beans are just tender.

Transfer the vegetables to a warmed serving dish and place the roasting tin on the hob. To make the gravy, stir the flour into the meat juices with a wooden spoon, then slowly add the stock, stirring well between each addition. Add the wine and redcurrant jelly and bring to the boil. Cook for 1 minute. If your gravy is still a little lumpy, whisk hard with a metal whisk until smooth. Season with salt and pepper and strain through a fine sieve into a warmed jug. Carve the lamb, discarding as much fat as possible, add any resting juices to the gravy and serve with fresh mint sauce (see page 22), the vegetables and gravy for pouring.

308
CALORIES
PER SERVING

lamb with spring vegetables and mint

SERVES 2
PREP: 15 MINUTES
COOK: 40 MINUTES

1 rack of lamb, extra
   trimmed (about 300g)
oil, for spraying or brushing
150g baby carrots, trimmed
   and halved if large
300g baby new potatoes,
   halved
200g baby courgettes,
   trimmed
flaked sea salt
ground black pepper

FOR THE FRESH MINT SAUCE
15g bunch of fresh mint,
   leaves stripped from
   stalks and finely chopped
1 tbsp caster sugar
1 tbsp white wine vinegar
4 tbsp just-boiled water

Look out for extra-trimmed racks of lamb for this recipe as all the hard work will have been done for you. They usually have 6 or 7 little rib bones that you can carve between to serve. Rack of lamb is fairly pricey, so keep this lovely dish for a special occasion.

Preheat the oven to 200°C/Fan 180°C/Gas 6. Season the lamb all over with a little salt and plenty of freshly ground black pepper. Brush or spray a sturdy, medium baking tray with oil and place over a medium-high heat.

Once the tin is hot but not smoking, carefully place the rack in the pan. Cook for 3½–4 minutes, turning the rack after each minute with tongs to ensure that every side of the lamb is lightly browned. Set aside on a board.

Add the carrots and potatoes to the roasting tin and spray or brush with oil. Season with salt and lots of freshly ground black pepper. Roast in the oven for 15 minutes.

Meanwhile, make the mint sauce. Put the chopped mint leaves in a small bowl and stir in the sugar and vinegar. Add 4 tablespoons of just-boiled water and stir well. Leave to cool.

Take the carrots and potatoes out of the oven and turn with a spatula. Add the courgettes and toss together. Transfer the lamb to the same tray and roast in the oven for 20 minutes for pink, medium lamb.

Take the tray out of the oven. Rest the lamb for 5 minutes and keep the vegetables warm. Carve the lamb into individual cutlets. Divide the vegetables between two warmed plates and top with the lamb. Season with a little salt and pepper and spoon over the mint sauce to serve.

355
CALORIES
PER SERVING

soy and ginger salmon with noodles

SERVES 4
**PREP: 15 MINUTES,
PLUS MARINATING TIME**
COOK: 15 MINUTES

75ml dark soy sauce
½ tsp dried chilli flakes
2 tbsp clear honey
20g chunk of fresh root
    ginger, peeled and cut
    into very thin strips
2 garlic cloves, thinly sliced
4 spring onions, thinly sliced
4 x 125g fresh salmon fillets
    (skin on)
1 red pepper, deseeded
    and thinly sliced
1 orange pepper, deseeded
    and thinly sliced
175g baby corn, trimmed
150g pack of cooked thick
    udon noodles
150g mangetout, trimmed
fresh coriander, to garnish
    (optional)

This is a brilliant lunch or supper dish that everyone seems to love and that takes just a few minutes to cook. It's also really delicious served cold as a salad for lunch the following day. You can find cooked noodles in sachets in the Chinese food section of the supermarket.

Mix the soy sauce, chilli flakes, honey, ginger, garlic and two of the spring onions in a medium freezer bag. Add the salmon fillets and toss until well coated in the marinade. Seal the bag and marinate the salmon in the fridge for at least 4 hours or preferably overnight. (It can be left in the marinade for up to 18 hours.)

Preheat the oven to 220°C/Fan 200°C/Gas 7. Scatter the peppers and baby corn over a large non-stick baking tray. Take the salmon fillets out of the marinade and place them, skin side down, among the vegetables. Reserve the marinade and bake the salmon for 10 minutes.

While the salmon is cooking, open the bag of noodles and put them in a colander in the sink. Slowly pour over a kettle full of just-boiled water, lifting the noodles with a fork to separate the strands, and drain.

Take the baking tray out of the oven and add the noodles and mangetout, using tongs or a spoon and fork. Pour over the reserved marinade. Return to the oven for a further 5 minutes, or until the vegetables are tender, the noodles are hot and the salmon is cooked. Sprinkle with the remaining spring onions and coriander to garnish, if you like.

430
CALORIES
PER SERVING

warm tuna niçoise

SERVES 2
PREP: 10 MINUTES
COOK: 25 MINUTES

400g baby new potatoes,
  halved
1 tbsp sunflower oil
1/4 tsp dried thyme
1/4 tsp dried rosemary
1/4 tsp flaked sea salt,
  plus extra to season
1/4 tsp ground black pepper,
  plus extra to season
2 x 120g fresh tuna steaks,
  each about 2cm thick
100g fine green beans,
  trimmed
250g cherry tomatoes
  on the vine
1 little gem lettuce, cut
  lengthways into wedges
40g pitted black olives
  in brine, drained
1 tbsp thick balsamic
  vinegar

If you like a traditional tuna niçoise, you will love this quick supper dish with fresh tuna, lots of vegetables and a light wholegrain mustard dressing. Serve with quartered hard-boiled eggs if you like – each medium egg contains 70 calories extra.

Preheat the oven to 220°C/Fan 200°C/Gas 7. Put the potatoes in a medium roasting tin and toss with the oil. Season with salt and black pepper and roast for 15 minutes.

Mix the dried herbs, salt and pepper. Season the tuna on both sides with the seasoning mix. Take the roasting tin out of the oven and turn the potatoes. Add the tuna and green beans and return to the oven for 5 minutes.

Take the tray out of the oven again and turn all the vegetables and the tuna. Add the tomatoes and bake for a further 3–5 minutes, or until the tuna is cooked to your taste.

While the tuna is cooking, make the dressing (see below) if using.

Divide the lettuce between two plates then add the cooked vegetables and olives, top with the tuna and drizzle over the balsamic vinegar to serve.

Vinaigrette: Put 2 teaspoons white wine vinegar, 1/2 teaspoon sugar and 1 teaspoon whole grain or Dijon mustard in a small bowl. Add a pinch of salt and a little freshly ground black pepper. Whisk to combine, then gradually whisk 2 tablespoons extra virgin olive oil into the vinegar mixture until the dressing has thickened slightly. Adjust seasoning to taste. Serves 2. Calories per serving: 107

293
CALORIES
PER SERVING

one-pan cooked breakfast

SERVES 2
PREP: 5 MINUTES
COOK: 18 MINUTES

oil, for spraying or brushing
2 reduced fat sausages
    (10% fat or less)
1 large beef tomato or
    slicing tomato, halved
10g butter, cut into
    small pieces
2 large eggs
2 smoked back bacon
    rashers, trimmed
    of visible fat
fresh watercress, to serve
flaked sea salt
ground black pepper

It's possible to make really creamy scrambled eggs in the oven if you follow this recipe for the easiest cooked breakfast ever – and there's hardly any washing up. Look out for 50% reduced-sugar ketchup to serve alongside – it contains 10 calories per tablespoon.

Preheat the oven to 200°C/Fan 180°C/Gas 6. Spray a non-stick baking tray with oil. Place the sausages and a small, shallow ovenproof pie dish on the tray (it will need to hold about 300ml) and bake for 5 minutes.

Take the tray out of the oven, turn the sausages over and add the tomato halves, cut side up, to the tray. Season with salt and pepper.

Put the butter in the warmed pie dish and break the eggs into the dish. Add a pinch of salt and whisk together with a small metal whisk. (If you don't have a small metal whisk, beat the eggs in a separate bowl then add to the dish.) Cover the dish with foil and return the tray to the oven for 5 minutes.

Take the tray out of the oven, turn the sausages and add the bacon. Stir the eggs with a fork then cover with foil again. Return to the oven for a further 5 minutes.

Take the tray out of the oven, turn the sausages and bacon, stir the eggs and return to the oven for a final 3 minutes or until the sausages are cooked and the eggs are scrambled to taste. Remember that the eggs will continue to cook in the heat of the dish.

Divide the scrambled eggs between two warmed plates. Add a sausage, tomato and rasher of bacon to each plate plus a few watercress sprigs. Serve immediately.

339
CALORIES
PER SERVING

easy apple and blackberry pie

SERVES 6
PREP: 10–15 MINUTES
COOK: 40–45 MINUTES

375g ready-rolled
   shortcrust pastry
1 tsp sunflower oil
300g frozen sliced Bramley
   cooking apples
200g frozen blackberries
1 tbsp cornflour
3 tbsp caster sugar
beaten egg, to glaze

This is a brilliant last-minute pudding, as most of the ingredients can be taken from the freezer and you don't need to be an expert cook to make it. It's heavy on fruit and short on pastry, which cuts the calories and the fat. If you use fresh rather than frozen fruit, you can reduce the cooking time by about 10 minutes.

Preheat the oven to 200°C/Fan 180°C/Gas 6. Unwrap and unroll the pastry onto a large non-stick baking tray brushed lightly with oil.

Mix the frozen fruit, cornflour and sugar together in a bowl or large freezer bag and leave to stand for 5 minutes. Arrange the fruit down the centre of the pastry from one short end to the other, leaving a 5cm gap at each side and at the ends. Pull up the sides of the pastry so it almost covers the fruit and tuck in the ends to seal all the fruit inside.

Brush the pastry all over with the beaten egg and bake the pie in the oven for 40–45 minutes or until golden brown and cooked through. Remove from the oven, and serve hot or cold in slices with fat-free fromage frais or half-fat crème fraiche, low-fat custard or single cream. (Don't forget to add the extra calories.)

wok

305
CALORIES
PER SERVING

chilli chicken stir-fry with rice

1 tbsp sunflower oil
3 boneless, skinless chicken breasts (about 450g), cut into roughly 2.5cm chunks
2 medium carrots (each about 100g), peeled and cut into roughly 5mm diagonal slices
1 large red pepper, deseeded and cut into roughly 3cm chunks
150g sugar snap peas, trimmed
3 tbsp Thai sweet chilli sauce
2 tbsp dark soy sauce, plus extra to serve
6 spring onions, trimmed leaving lots of green, and cut into roughly 2cm lengths, plus extra to garnish
250g sachet pre-cooked long grain rice

Tip: Look out for sachets of cooked rice in the supermarket – the rice only needs reheating for a few minutes and is perfect for one-pan dishes like this.

Thai sweet chilli dipping sauce and soy sauce combine to make a quick and convenient sauce for this colourful stir-fry – and using pre-cooked rice saves using an extra pan.

Place a large non-stick frying pan or wok over a medium-high heat. Pour the sunflower oil into the pan and as soon as it is hot, add the chicken and stir-fry for 2 minutes, or until very lightly coloured all over.

Scatter the carrots, pepper and peas into the pan with the chicken and stir-fry for a further 4–5 minutes, until almost tender.

Pour over the chilli and soy sauces, add the spring onions and toss together for a few seconds, then add the rice and cook for a further 3 minutes, or until the rice and chicken are hot throughout, stirring continuously.

467
CALORIES
PER SERVING

chicken and ham
wok lasagne

SERVES 4

PREP: 10 MINUTES

COOK: 12–15 MINUTES

oil, for spraying or brushing
1 medium onion, finely
    chopped
600g boneless, skinless
    chicken breasts (about
    4 small breasts), cut
    into roughly 2cm chunks
2 garlic cloves, crushed
    or finely grated
100ml white wine
1 chicken stock cube
150ml just-boiled water
3 tbsp cornflour
300ml semi-skimmed milk
2–3 fresh egg lasagne
    sheets (about 125g),
    each cut into 3 strips
    widthways
100g sliced smoked ham,
    cut into 2cm-wide strips
100g young spinach leaves
100g ready grated
    mozzarella (from a
    packet)
20g Parmesan cheese,
    finely grated
large mixed salad, to serve

Tip: If you can't find fresh
lasagne in your local shops,
cook dried lasagne in
boiling water until almost
tender instead.

It's hard to believe that a lasagne could be cooked in a wok, but it's perfectly possible with this speedy one-pot pasta dish. Use fresh lasagne sheets – you'll find them in the chiller aisle – and freeze any leftover sheets for next time.

Brush or spray a little oil into a large non-stick, flameproof wok and place over a medium heat. Add the onion and chicken pieces and stir-fry for 3 minutes, or until very lightly coloured.

Stir in the garlic then the wine. Crumble the stock cube over and stir until it starts to dissolve. Add the just-boiled water, bring to a gentle simmer and cook for 1 minute.

While the liquid is simmering, stir 3 tablespoons of the milk into the cornflour in a bowl to make a smooth paste. Pour the rest of the milk and the cornflour mixture into the pan with the chicken and bring back to a gentle simmer, stirring frequently. Rinse the pasta strips quickly under cold water.

Add the ham, spinach leaves and pasta to the wok and simmer gently for 5 minutes, stirring frequently until the pasta is tender. Preheat the grill to its hottest setting.

Scatter the grated mozzarella and Parmesan cheese on top of the lasagne. Season with black pepper and grill for 3–5 minutes, or until the cheese is melted and beginning to brown. Make sure your wok doesn't have wooden or plastic handles, so it can go under the grill. Alternatively, transfer the lasagne to a suitable dish before grilling, but make sure you warm the dish before you add the lasagne. Serve with a large mixed salad.

429
CALORIES
PER SERVING

coconut chicken curry

SERVES 4
PREP: 15 MINUTES
COOK: 40 MINUTES

8 boneless, skinless chicken
thighs (about 675g),
trimmed of visible fat
and cut in half
1 tbsp sunflower oil
1 medium onion,
roughly chopped
4 garlic cloves, thinly sliced
4 tbsp medium curry paste
2 tbsp cornflour
250ml cold water
400ml can reduced-fat
coconut milk
1 tbsp Thai fish sauce
(nam pla)
300g potatoes (ideally
Maris Piper), peeled
and cut into roughly
3cm chunks
150g fine green beans,
trimmed
1 large red pepper,
deseeded and cut into
roughly 3cm chunks
1 large green pepper,
deseeded and cut into
roughly 3cm chunks
2–3 tbsp fresh lime juice
flaked sea salt
ground black pepper

This creamy curry features both Indian and south-east Asian flavours and is inspired by popular chicken curries made in the Philippines. The addition of potatoes, peppers and beans means you don't need to serve it with additional rice or breads.

Season the chicken thighs with salt and pepper. Heat the oil in a large, wide non-stick saucepan or sauté pan and fry the chicken in two batches for 2–3 minutes, until lightly browned. Transfer to a plate and set aside.

Add the onion to the pan and stir-fry for 3 minutes or until it's starting to soften. Stir in the garlic and curry paste and cook for a few seconds more.

Mix the cornflour with 2 tablespoons of the cold water in a bowl to make a thin paste. Pour the coconut milk and remaining water into the pan with the onion and stir in the cornflour mixture and Thai fish sauce.

Return the chicken pieces to the pan along with any resting juices. Add the potatoes, cover loosely with a lid or a large piece of foil and bring to a gentle simmer. Cook over a medium heat for 15 minutes. Remove the lid a couple of times, stir and turn the chicken as it cooks.

When the 15 minutes is up, stir in the beans and peppers. Cover loosely and cook for a further 10 minutes, or until the chicken and vegetables are tender, stirring frequently. Remove from the heat and stir in the lime juice to taste. The curry should taste creamy, but also hot and slightly sour.

286
CALORIES
PER SERVING

SERVES 4
PREP: 10 MINUTES
COOK: 18 MINUTES

12 ready-made meatballs
(about 300g, 20% fat
or less)
2 pak choi
(each about 100g)
2 medium carrots (each
about 100g), peeled
and cut into roughly
5mm diagonal slices
1 medium red onion,
peeled and cut into
12 thin wedges
1 large red pepper,
deseeded and cut into
roughly 3cm chunks
150g mangetout, trimmed
5 tbsp hoisin sauce
(from a jar)

hoisin meatball stir-fry

This is a stir-fry that's cheap and quick to cook. Meatballs can be fairly high in fat, but that means you don't need any extra fat to stir-fry the vegetables. Serve with a portion of rice or noodles, or just as it is.

Place a large non-stick wok or frying pan over a medium-high heat and add the meatballs. Cook (without additional fat) for 10 minutes, turning regularly until browned all over and cooked through.

While the meatballs are cooking, trim the pak choi and then cut into roughly 2.5cm-wide slices. Separate the green leaves from the whitish stalks. Add the carrots, onion, pepper and the pak choi stalks to the wok with the meatballs and stir-fry for 5 minutes. Add the mangetout and green pak choi leaves and cook for a further 2 minutes.

Spoon over the hoisin sauce and toss with the meatballs and vegetables. Cook for a further minute, stirring and tossing until hot throughout.

346
CALORIES
PER SERVING

creamy pork, apples and cabbage

SERVES 4

PREP: 15 MINUTES

COOK: 15–18 MINUTES

500g pork tenderloin
   (fillet), trimmed and cut
   into roughly 2cm slices
1 small Savoy cabbage
   (about 475g)
300ml cold water
1 tbsp sunflower oil
1 medium onion, cut into
   thin wedges
2 small red eating apples,
   quartered, cored and
   sliced
200ml dry cider
2 tbsp cornflour
150ml hot pork or chicken
   stock (made with ½ cube)
2 tsp wholegrain or
   Dijon mustard
300g can peeled new
   potatoes, drained
   and halved (180g
   drained weight)
3 tbsp half-fat crème fraiche
flaked sea salt
ground black pepper

Flat-freeze the cooked,
cooled pork, vegetables
and sauce in two large
freezer bags. Thaw
overnight in the fridge.
Reheat in a large wok over
a medium heat, stirring
frequently until piping hot.

Tender pork in a creamy sauce with sautéed apples, cabbage and potatoes – all cooked in a wok! It's best to get everything ready before you begin to cook, as it doesn't take long.

Season the pork generously with salt and pepper, and put to one side.

Remove any damaged leaves from the cabbage and cut in half. Cut out the tough central core and then thinly shred the leaves. You should end up with about 375g of shredded cabbage.

Place the cabbage in a large non-stick wok on a medium-high heat, pour over 300ml cold water, cover with a lid or a large piece of foil and bring to the boil. Cook the cabbage for 3½–5 minutes, or until just tender, stirring once. Drain in a colander.

Pour 2 teaspoons of the oil into the same wok and place over a high heat. Fry the pork in two batches for 2–3 minutes until well browned on both sides but not quite cooked through. Tip onto a plate, set aside and return the wok to the heat. Add the remaining oil and fry the onion for 3 minutes, then add the apple slices and cook for a further 2 minutes, or until the onion and apples are lightly browned.

Mix 3 tablespoons of the cider with the cornflour in a bowl until smooth. Return the pork to the pan, add the remaining cider, the stock, mustard, cornflour mixture and potatoes. Bring to a simmer and cook for 2 minutes, stirring frequently. Stir in the crème fraiche and season to taste with salt and pepper.

Pile the cabbage on top of the bubbling sauce and cover once more. Simmer for a further 2 minutes, or until the pork is cooked and the cabbage is hot. Serve in wide bowls.

162
CALORIES
PER SERVING

ginger and chilli
prawn wraps

SERVES 2

PREP: 10 MINUTES

COOK: 5 MINUTES

FOR THE WRAPS

1 little gem lettuce,
leaves separated

1 medium carrot, peeled
and cut into thin sticks

1 red pepper, deseeded
and cut into thin sticks

2 spring onions, cut into
thin sticks

small handful of fresh
mint leaves (optional)

small handful of fresh
coriander leaves
(optional)

lime wedges, for squeezing

FOR THE PRAWNS

6 Szechuan peppercorns
(Sichuan pepper) or
12 black peppercorns

15g chunk of fresh root
ginger, peeled and cut
into fine matchsticks

1 tsp dried chilli flakes, plus
a pinch extra to serve

200g raw, peeled king
prawns, thawed if frozen

2 tbsp hoisin sauce

Tip: Szechuan peppercorns
are mouth-tingling spicy,
but black peppercorns
work well too.

If you like Chinese-style duck pancakes, you are sure to
enjoy my healthy take on the classic combination. I've used
low-calorie prawns and lettuce wraps rather than duck and
pancakes, but there's still hoisin sauce for dribbling and
crunchy vegetables for piling up on the prawns. It's all cooked
in one pan, but you'll need a couple of small dishes for serving
the prawns and sauce separately; otherwise, combine them
both in the wok and serve on plates with the vegetables.

Separate the lettuce leaves and place them on a serving board
or platter. Add piles of the other vegetables to the board and
scatter with mint and coriander leaves, if using.

Lightly crush the peppercorns in a pestle and mortar and
tip into a non-stick wok or frying pan. Place over a high heat
and cook for a few seconds, then add the ginger, chilli flakes
and prawns. Stir-fry for 2 minutes, or until the prawns are hot,
cooked and pink throughout. Tip into a heatproof bowl and
set aside.

Discard any liquid from the pan then return to the heat and add
the hoisin sauce and 2 tablespoons of cold water. Heat for a few
seconds until thoroughly combined, stirring continuously, then
pour into another small heatproof bowl.

Serve the hot prawns in lettuce leaf wraps with the vegetable
strips and herbs, drizzled with the warm hoisin dressing. Squeeze
over a little lime juice if you like.

286
CALORIES
PER SERVING

goan fish curry

SERVES 4
PREP: 15 MINUTES
COOK: 15–18 MINUTES

1 tbsp sunflower oil
1 medium onion, thinly
    sliced
1 red pepper, deseeded
    and cut into roughly
    3cm chunks
1 green pepper, deseeded
    and cut into roughly
    3cm chunks
2 garlic cloves, crushed
    or finely grated
20g chunk of fresh root
    ginger, peeled and
    finely grated
2 tbsp medium curry paste
4 ripe tomatoes, roughly
    chopped
1 long green chilli, trimmed
    and thinly sliced
    (do not deseed)
1 tbsp white wine vinegar
    or cider vinegar
150ml cold water
200ml coconut milk
1 tsp flaked sea salt
1 tsp caster sugar
500g thick, skinless white
    fish fillet, such as cod,
    haddock or pollack, cut
    into roughly 3cm chunks
warmed chapatis (optional)

Tip: This recipe doesn't
use reduced-fat coconut
milk, just half a can of the
full-fat version. Flat-freeze
any leftover coconut milk
for up to one month and
thaw at room temperature
before using the same day.

I love this curry. It's spicy, sour and sweet, a really great way
of incorporating fish into your diet, and it's very quick to cook.
If you don't like much heat, deseed the chilli before slicing
and the sauce will be much milder, but just as delicious.
Chapatis are lower in calories than naan bread and make
a good accompaniment.

Heat the oil in a large non-stick wok or frying pan over a medium
heat and add the onion. Fry for 3 minutes, stirring frequently
until softened and lightly browned then add the pepper, garlic
and ginger and cook for a further 2 minutes, stirring.

Stir the curry paste into the pan and fry with the onion, garlic
and ginger for a few seconds, stirring continuously. Add the
chopped tomatoes and chilli to the same pan and stir in the
vinegar and 4 tablespoons of the water. Cook for 3–4 minutes,
or until the tomatoes are well softened, stirring frequently.

Pour the coconut milk into the pan and add the remaining
water, salt and sugar. Bring to a gentle simmer and cook
for 2 minutes, stirring occasionally.

Place the fish on top of the curry sauce, cover with a lid or a
large piece of foil and simmer for 3–5 minutes, or until the fish
is just cooked. The cooking time of the fish will depend on how
large your pieces are and how dense the fish. Give the pan a
little shake every now and then as it cooks, but try not to stir,
as you could break up the fish. Serve immediately with warm
chapatis, if you like, but don't forget to add the extra calories.

367
CALORIES
PER SERVING

paneer and vegetable curry

SERVES 4
PREP: 20 MINUTES
COOK: 35–40 MINUTES

1 tbsp sunflower oil
225g paneer, drained
    and cut into roughly
    2cm cubes
1 tsp cumin seeds
2 medium onions, sliced
3 garlic cloves, crushed
    or finely grated
25g chunk of fresh root
    ginger, peeled and
    finely grated
1 long green chilli, finely
    chopped (do not deseed)
1 tbsp medium curry
    powder
400g can chopped
    tomatoes
400g potatoes (ideally
    Maris Piper), peeled
    and cut into roughly
    2.5cm chunks
500ml cold water
½ tsp fine sea salt,
    plus extra to season
1 tsp caster sugar
100g young spinach leaves
100g frozen peas
ground black pepper

Flat-freeze the cooked
and cooled curry in labelled
zip-seal bags for up to
1 month. Cook from frozen
or thaw in the fridge overnight.
Reheat in a large, wide-based
saucepan, stirring gently
until piping hot.

Paneer is an Indian cheese that cooks beautifully and retains its texture. This is one vegetarian dish that even meat lovers will enjoy. It's quite fiery, so if you prefer your curry a little milder, deseed the chilli before chopping.

Place a large non-stick wok or frying pan over a medium heat. Brush with a little of the oil, then fry the paneer in two batches for 3–4 minutes, turning regularly until the cubes are lightly browned. Transfer to a plate, set aside and return the wok to the hob.

Add the remaining sunflower oil to the wok or pan and fry the cumin seeds over a medium-high heat for a few seconds, stirring. Add the onions, garlic, ginger and green chilli and cook for 6–8 minutes, stirring regularly until the onions are well softened. Sprinkle over the curry powder and cook for about 30 seconds, stirring.

Tip the chopped tomatoes into the pan, add the potatoes, water and salt. Season with plenty of black pepper. Bring the sauce to a gentle simmer, stirring continuously. Cover and cook the sauce for about 20 minutes, or until the potatoes are tender. Don't let the sauce boil furiously and stir it frequently as it simmers, especially towards the end of the cooking time.

When the curry sauce is ready, stir in the sugar, the spinach leaves (a handful at a time) and the frozen peas. Cook for a further 2–3 minutes until hot, adding a little extra water if needed, then add the paneer and heat through gently. Check the seasoning – you may want a little extra salt or pepper – and serve.

277

CALORIES
PER SERVING

vegetable pakoras

SERVES 4
PREP: 10 MINUTES
COOK: 12 MINUTES

350g frozen mixed
    vegetables, such
    as peas, sweetcorn,
    carrots and beans
125g gram flour (chickpea
    flour), sifted
20g bunch of fresh
    coriander, leaves
    finely chopped
1 tsp fine sea salt
1 tsp hot chilli powder
½ tsp ground turmeric
100ml warm water
500–650ml sunflower oil,
    for frying
cucumber yoghurt (see
    right), mango chutney,
    lime wedges and fresh
    coriander, to serve

Freeze the cooked and
cooled pakoras in a freezer
bag for up to 1 month.
Reheat from frozen on a
baking tray in a preheated
oven at 200°C/Fan 180°C/
Gas 6 for about 10 minutes
or until piping hot.

Using frozen vegetables for these pakoras is both cost effective and quick. Serve as a light meal with dips (see minted cucumber yoghurt, below) and a salad, if you like. It might seem strange to include deep-frying in a low calorie cookbook but overall the meal remains low in calories and that's what really counts.

Put the vegetables into a sieve and pour a kettleful of just-boiled water over them. Leave to drain for 2–3 minutes then tip into a large mixing bowl. Add the gram flour, salt, chilli powder and turmeric and toss lightly together. Stir in the warm water, stirring continuously until the vegetables are coated with a thick batter.

Pour the oil into a wok or wide-based saucepan until it is roughly 2.5cm deep. Heat the oil to 160°C on a cooking thermometer. Do not allow the oil to overheat or leave hot oil unattended.

Take a heaped dessertspoon of the batter and drop it very gently and carefully into the hot oil. You will need to push it off the spoon with a second spoon. Continue adding batter until you have 4 pakoras frying at the same time. Cook them for about 3 minutes, turning once or twice with a metal slotted spoon or tongs, until crisp and golden brown.

Lift out of the oil with the tongs or spoon and drain on kitchen paper. Allow the oil to return to the correct temperature and continue cooking the remaining pakoras in two more batches, exactly the same way. Serve warm with cucumber yoghurt, mango chutney (about 50 calories per tablespoon), lime or lemon wedges, and fresh coriander.

Minted cucumber yoghurt: Mix 150g pot fat-free natural yoghurt with a third of a cucumber, diced, and 3 heaped tablespoons finely chopped fresh mint. Serves 4. Calories per serving: 25

saucepan

140
CALORIES
PER SERVING

leek and potato soup

SERVES 6
PREP: 10 MINUTES
COOK: 35 MINUTES

15g butter
1 tbsp sunflower oil
2 medium onions,
    roughly chopped
3 medium leeks (about
    450g in total), trimmed
    and thinly sliced
500g potatoes (ideally
    Maris Piper), peeled
    and cut into roughly
    2cm chunks
1 litre cold water
1 chicken or vegetable
    stock cube
100ml semi-skimmed milk
flaked sea salt
ground black pepper

Flat-freeze the cooked and
cooled soup in labelled zip-
seal bags for up to 6 months.
Put the frozen soup into a
saucepan and thaw gently,
stirring as it melts. As soon
as all the soup has defrosted,
bring to a simmer and cook,
stirring frequently, until
piping hot. Add a little
extra water if necessary.
Alternatively, thaw in the
fridge overnight and reheat
in a saucepan or microwave.

**Heavy on leeks, cheap and filling, this soup makes for a
welcome meal on a cold day and it can be reheated from
frozen. When the weather is hot, serve it chilled with a
swirl of half-fat crème fraiche and a sprinkling of chives
for a delicious Vichysoisse.**

Melt the butter with the oil in a large non-stick saucepan
over a low heat and fry the onions and leeks for 8–10 minutes,
stirring frequently until well softened.

Add the potatoes to the pan and stir in the water and stock
cube. Bring to the boil, then reduce the heat slightly and
simmer uncovered for about 20 minutes, or until all the
vegetables are very soft, stirring occasionally.

Remove the pan from the heat and stir in the milk. Remove
from the heat and blitz with a stick blender until smooth.
(Alternatively, cool for a few minutes then transfer in batches
to a liquidiser or food processor and blend until smooth.)
Season with salt and pepper to taste and reheat gently, adding
extra water if necessary until the right consistency is reached.

108
CALORIES
PER SERVING

carrot, sweet potato and coriander soup

SERVES 6
PREP: 15 MINUTES
COOK: 30 MINUTES

1 tbsp sunflower oil
2 medium onions,
    roughly chopped
5 medium carrots (about
    500g), peeled and cut
    into roughly 1.5cm slices
1 sweet potato (about
    300g), peeled and cut
    into roughly 2cm chunks
2 garlic cloves, thinly sliced
1 tsp ground coriander
¼ tsp hot chilli powder
1.3 litres chicken or
    vegetable stock (made
    with 1 stock cube)
20g bunch of fresh
    coriander, including
    the stalks, roughly
    chopped
flaked sea salt
ground black pepper

Flat-freeze the cooked
and cooled soup in labelled
zip-seal bags for up to
6 months. Put the frozen
soup into a saucepan and
thaw gently, stirring as it
melts. As soon as all the
soup has defrosted, bring
to a simmer and cook,
stirring frequently, until
piping hot. Add a little
extra water if necessary.
Alternatively, thaw in the
fridge overnight and reheat
in a saucepan or microwave.

I'm a huge fan of carrot and coriander soup, and chunks of sweet potato bring a new dimension, making it even more delicious. Blitzing the coriander stalks as well as the leaves adds lots of extra flavour to the soup.

Heat the oil in a large non-stick saucepan and gently fry the onions with the carrots and sweet potato chunks for 10 minutes, stirring occasionally. Add the garlic, ground coriander and chilli powder and cook for a further 30 seconds, stirring continuously.

Pour over the stock and bring to the boil. Reduce the heat to a simmer and cook for about 20 minutes, or until the carrots are very soft, stirring occasionally. Remove from the heat.

Blitz the soup with a stick blender until very smooth. (If you don't have a stick blender, allow the soup to cool for a few minutes then blend in a food processor or liquidiser instead.) Add the coriander and blitz once more. Add a little extra water if needed, until the perfect consistency is reached. Season with salt and pepper to taste. Reheat gently just before serving, stirring continuously.

356

CALORIES PER SERVING

hob-top chicken biryani

SERVES 5

PREP: 15 MINUTES

COOK: 40 MINUTES

2 tbsp sunflower oil

6 boneless, skinless chicken thighs (about 500g), trimmed of visible fat and each cut into 3 pieces

2 medium onions, thinly sliced

3 tbsp medium curry paste

2 medium carrots (each about 100g), peeled and cut into roughly 5mm diagonal slices

½ medium cauliflower (about 300g), cut into small florets

100g fine green beans, trimmed and cut into 3cm lengths

800ml hot chicken stock (made with 1 chicken cube)

150g basmati rice, rinsed and drained

150g frozen peas

15g bunch of fresh coriander, leaves roughly chopped

fat-free natural yoghurt and mango chutney, to serve

Tip: You'll need to add 8 calories for each tablespoon of fat-free yoghurt and 50 calories for each tablespoon of mango chutney.

This is a super, really filling dish. I like to serve it straight from the saucepan with fat-free natural yoghurt and mango chutney, plus a generous scattering of chopped coriander.

Heat the oil in a large, wide-based, non-stick saucepan or sauté pan and fry the chicken and onions over a high heat for 8–10 minutes, stirring frequently until the onions are golden brown. Reduce the heat to medium and stir in the curry paste. Cook for 1 minute, stirring continuously.

Add the carrots, cauliflower, beans and stock. Bring to the boil then reduce the heat, cover loosely and simmer gently for 12–15 minutes, stirring occasionally, until the vegetables are just tender.

Remove the lid, add the rice and continue to cook uncovered for a further 10 minutes or until the rice is tender, stirring occasionally and adding the peas after 7 minutes. (Add a splash more water if all the liquid is absorbed before the rice is ready.)

Sprinkle with coriander and serve with fat-free yoghurt and mango chutney (see tip).

328

CALORIES
PER SERVING

harissa chicken
and bulgur pilaf

SERVES 4
PREP: 10 MINUTES
COOK: 15 MINUTES

2 medium courgettes,
  halved lengthways
  and cut into roughly
  2cm slices
1 red pepper, deseeded
  and cut into roughly
  2.5cm chunks
1 orange pepper, deseeded
  and cut into roughly
  2.5cm chunks
1 medium red onion,
  cut into 12 wedges
2 tbsp mild olive oil
  or sunflower oil
2 boneless, skinless chicken
  breasts (each about 175g),
  cut into roughly
  2cm chunks
1 tsp ground coriander
1 tsp ground cumin
1 tbsp harissa paste
  (from a jar)
4 garlic cloves, thinly sliced
500ml hot chicken stock
  (made with 1 chicken
  cube)
150g bulgur wheat, rinsed
  in a sieve and drained
2 tbsp fresh lemon juice
flaked sea salt
ground black pepper
fresh coriander leaves,
  roughly chopped, to
  garnish (optional)
lightly dressed green salad,
  to serve

Warming harissa paste adds colour and spicy heat to this simple pilaf. It is packed with vegetables, so you'll only need two chicken breasts for a really filling supper.

Put the courgettes, peppers and onion in a large wide-based saucepan or sauté pan and toss with the oil until well coated. Season with salt and lots of black pepper.

Place over a high heat and stir-fry the vegetables for 3 minutes, or until lightly browned but not cooked through. Add the chicken and stir-fry for a further 2 minutes. Stir in the dried coriander, cumin, harissa paste and garlic and cook for 20 seconds, stirring.

Pour over the stock, add the bulgur wheat, and bring to a simmer. Cook for 10 minutes or until the bulgur wheat is tender and the liquid is well reduced and almost all absorbed, stirring frequently, especially towards the end of the cooking time.

Stir in the lemon juice and sprinkle with coriander (if using) just before serving with a lightly dressed green salad.

394

CALORIES
PER SERVING

simple sausage stew

SERVES 4
PREP: 10 MINUTES
COOK: 35 MINUTES

1 tbsp sunflower oil
12 good quality pork
     chipolatas
1 large onion, thinly sliced
2 yellow peppers, deseeded
     and cut into roughly
     3cm chunks
2 medium courgettes, cut
     into roughly 2cm slices
2 garlic cloves, crushed
¼ tsp dried flaked chillies
1 tsp dried oregano
400g can chopped
     tomatoes with herbs
400g can cannellini beans,
     drained and rinsed
2 tbsp tomato purée
250ml chicken or pork stock
     (made with 1 stock cube)
150ml red wine or water
flaked sea salt
ground black pepper
fresh flat-leaf parsley,
     roughly chopped,
     to garnish (optional)

Freeze the cooked and
cooled stew in a shallow
freezer-proof container
for up to 3 months. Thaw
overnight in the fridge and
reheat in a large saucepan
or microwave, stirring
frequently until piping hot.

If the weather turns chilly, this spicy stew is just the thing. Choose chipolata sausages with a high meat content – about 90% is perfect. Using chipolatas means the recipe is easy to divide by four, and the courgettes and beans make it more filling and add extra fibre.

Heat the oil in a large, wide-based non-stick saucepan, sauté pan or flameproof casserole and fry the sausages gently for 10 minutes, turning them every now and then until browned all over. Transfer to a plate and set aside.

Put the onion and peppers in the same pan and fry over a medium heat for 3 minutes until beginning to soften, stirring often. Add the courgettes, garlic, chilli flakes and oregano and cook for a further 2 minutes, stirring.

Stir in the tomatoes, beans, tomato purée, stock and wine or water. Return the chipolatas to the pan. Bring to a simmer. Reduce the heat slightly and leave to simmer gently for 20 minutes, stirring occasionally. Season well with salt and pepper and garnish with chopped parsley (if using) just before serving.

414

CALORIES
PER SERVING

bolognese pasta pot

SERVES 5
PREP: 10 MINUTES
COOK: 40 MINUTES

500g lean minced beef
   (10% fat or less)
1 large onion, finely
   chopped
150g closed-cup
   mushrooms, thickly sliced
2 garlic cloves, crushed
150ml red wine or
   beef stock
1 litre beef stock (made
   with 1 beef cube)
400g can chopped
   tomatoes
2 tbsp tomato purée
1½ tsp dried oregano
250g dried penne pasta
flaked sea salt
ground black pepper
large mixed salad, to serve

Freeze the cooked and
cooled pasta and sauce
in single-serving freezer-
proof containers for up to
1 month. Thaw overnight
in the fridge then reheat in
the microwave on high for
3–4 minutes per serving,
or until piping hot.

Tip: Some supermarket
packs of beef are sold as
450g portions, so you can
use that instead of 500g.
It will reduce the calories
by 18 per serving.

Cook your pasta with the sauce and you'll have a delicious,
easy supper and only one pan to wash. Sprinkle with grated
Parmesan cheese if you like, but you'll need to add an extra
42 calories for every 10 grams.

Place a large non-stick saucepan over a medium heat and
add the minced beef and onion. Cook together for 3 minutes,
stirring the beef and squishing it against the sides of the pan
to break up the mince. Add the mushrooms and garlic and
cook for a further 3 minutes, stirring frequently.

Add the wine or stock, then 500ml of the beef stock. Tip
the tomatoes into the pan and stir in the tomato purée and
oregano. Season with salt and plenty of black pepper. Bring
to a simmer and cook for 15 minutes, stirring occasionally.
Remove the lid and stir in the remaining stock. Bring to a
simmer and add the pasta, stirring to separate the pieces.

Cook uncovered for 20 minutes, or until the pasta is tender
and most of the stock has been absorbed. Stir frequently,
especially towards the end of the cooking time. (If your stock
is absorbed before the pasta is ready, just add a splash more
water and continue cooking.) Adjust the seasoning to taste
and serve with a large mixed salad.

365
CALORIES
PER SERVING

italian fish stew

SERVES 4

PREP: 15 MINUTES

COOK: 30 MINUTES

1 tbsp mild olive oil
  or sunflower oil
1 medium onion,
  thinly sliced
2 garlic cloves, thinly sliced
1 tsp coriander seeds,
  lightly crushed
½ tsp dried chilli flakes
1 tsp dried oregano
2 x 400g cans chopped
  tomatoes with herbs
150ml red wine
800ml water
175g dried pasta, such
  as penne or fusilli
2 medium-large courgettes,
  halved lengthways
  and cut into roughly
  1.5cm slices
75g black olives, preferably
  Kalamata, drained and
  pitted, if preferred
400g thick, skinless white
  fish fillet, such as cod,
  haddock or pollack, cut
  into roughly 4cm chunks
1 tsp flaked sea salt
ground black pepper
chopped parsley leaves,
  to garnish (optional)

Tip: You can crush the coriander seeds in a pestle and mortar or use 1 tsp ground coriander instead if you prefer.

A warming, rich stew with bags of flavour. The pasta cooks in the tomato sauce and the fish is added for the last few minutes. Choose a heavy, wide-based pan so everything cooks evenly, and use short pasta rather than spaghetti or tagliatelle for the best results.

Heat the olive or sunflower oil in a large non-stick, wide-based saucepan or flameproof casserole and gently fry the onion for 5 minutes or until well softened, stirring frequently. Add the garlic, spices and oregano and cook for a few seconds. Stir in the tomatoes, red wine and water and bring to a simmer.

Add the pasta and simmer for 15 minutes, or until it is almost tender, stirring frequently. Add the courgettes and cook for a further 5 minutes, stirring occasionally. Season well with the salt and lots of ground black pepper. Stir in the olives and place the fish pieces on top.

Cover and cook for 5–7 minutes, or until the fish is just cooked and beginning to flake. (The cooking time will depend on the thickness of your fish pieces.) Scatter parsley over the top, if using, and serve. (Watch out for stones if using unpitted olives.)

134
CALORIES
PER SERVING

caponata with cannellini beans

SERVES 6

PREP: 15 MINUTES

COOK: 1 HOUR 10 MINUTES

oil, for spraying
2 medium aubergines
    (each about 225g),
    cut into roughly
    2cm chunks
1 large red onion,
    thinly sliced
3 slender celery sticks,
    trimmed and thinly sliced
3 garlic cloves, thinly sliced
2 x 400g cans chopped
    tomatoes
50g light soft brown sugar
2 tbsp red wine vinegar
400g can cannellini beans,
    rinsed and drained
300ml cold water
1 tbsp pine nuts
flaked sea salt
ground black pepper
extra virgin olive oil and
    basil leaves, to serve

Flat-freeze the cooked
and cooled caponata for
up to 3 months. Thaw
overnight in the fridge and
then reheat in a wide-based
saucepan or the microwave,
stirring frequently until
piping hot.

Tip: Stir in 2 tablespoons of
drained capers (from a jar)
with the aubergine for an
even more authentic flavour.

Caponata is a thick aubergine stew usually made with lots of olive oil. I've used spray oil for mine, to drastically cut the calories. Cooked long and slow, the aubergines should be silky soft when the caponata is ready. Serve warm or cold with a mixed salad and flatbread, or pile onto hot toasted ciabatta.

Place a large, wide-based non-stick saucepan over a high heat and spray with oil. Add half the aubergine, season with salt and pepper and spray with more oil. Fry for about 4 minutes, or until lightly browned all over, stirring frequently. Tip onto a plate and set aside. Repeat with the remaining aubergine.

Return the saucepan to the heat and add the onion and celery. Spray with more oil and cook for 5 minutes, stirring occasionally. Add the garlic and cook for 30 seconds, stirring, then tip the chopped tomatoes into the pan. Stir in the sugar and vinegar and bring to a gentle simmer. Cover loosely and cook for 15 minutes, stirring occasionally.

Add the aubergines, cannellini beans and water and return to a gentle simmer. Cover loosely again and cook for a further 30 minutes, then remove the lid and cook for 10 minutes more or until very thick, stirring frequently, especially towards the end of the cooking time. Add a splash of water if needed.

Stir in the pine nuts and season with a good pinch of salt and plenty of ground black pepper. Serve warm or leave to cool, cover, chill and eat within 3 days. Drizzle with a little extra virgin olive oil and garnish with basil leaves to serve, but don't forget to add 27 calories for each teaspoon of olive oil.

Caponata on toast: Cut 1 x 350g ciabatta loaf in half horizontally and then cut in half again to make 4 rectangular pieces. Toast on both sides and then rub the cut side with half a garlic clove. Divide between plates and spoon the warm caponata on top. Garnish with basil and drizzle with 1 teaspoon olive oil. Serves 4. Calories per serving: 378

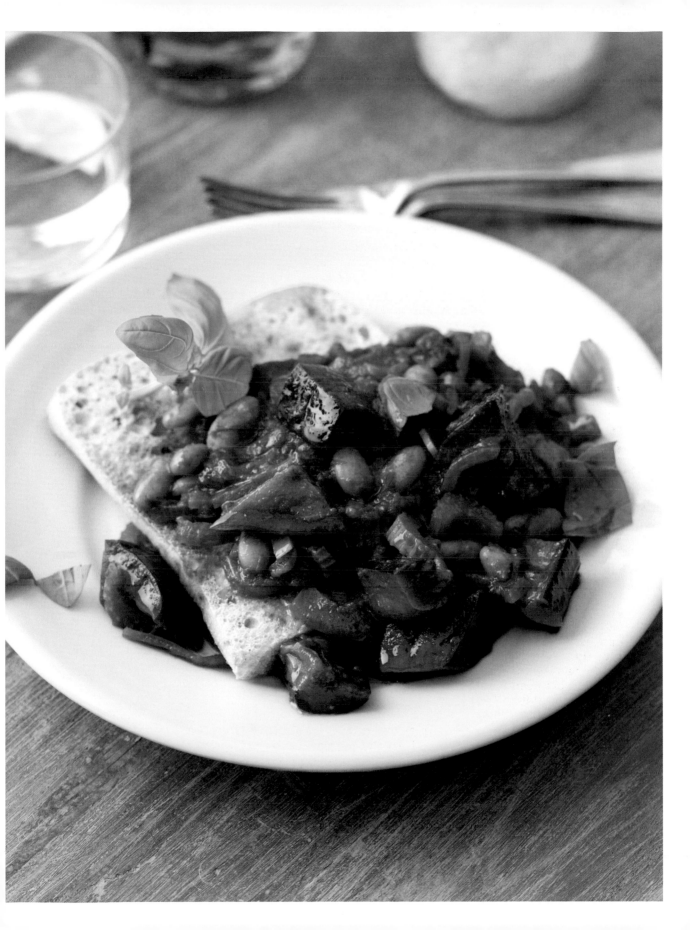

378
CALORIES
PER SERVING

coconut and sweet potato dhal

SERVES 4
PREP: 10 MINUTES
COOK: 30–35 MINUTES

1 tbsp sunflower oil
1 medium onion,
   finely chopped
2 garlic cloves, thinly sliced
1 tbsp medium curry
   powder
200g dried red split lentils
400ml can reduced-fat
   coconut milk
½ tsp fine sea salt,
   plus extra to season
600ml water
500g sweet potatoes,
   peeled and cut into
   roughly 3cm chunks
1 bay leaf
150g green beans,
   trimmed and halved
2 tbsp fresh lime
   or lemon juice
ground black pepper
natural yoghurt, mango
   chutney, lime wedges
   and fresh coriander
   leaves, to serve

Lentils are cheap, filling and full of fibre and this simple dhal is quick to cook but tastes very luxurious thanks to the coconut milk. Sweet potatoes and green beans add texture and it's really delicious served hot or just warm with a large crunchy salad, fat-free yoghurt (add 8 calories per tablespoon) and pickles.

Heat the oil in a large non-stick saucepan and fry the onion over a low heat for 5 minutes, stirring frequently until softened and very lightly browned, adding the garlic for the last minute of cooking time. Stir in the curry powder and cook for a few more seconds.

Add the lentils, coconut milk, salt and water. Stir in the sweet potato, add the bay leaf and bring to the boil. Reduce the heat to a simmer and cook the lentils for 15 minutes, stirring frequently.

Add the green beans and cook for a further 10–15 minutes or until the dhal is thick, stirring frequently. Add an extra splash of water if the dhal thickens too much before the lentils are softened.

Stir in the lime or lemon juice and adjust the seasoning to taste. Serve with yoghurt, mango chutney (about 50 calories per tablespoon), lime wedges for squeezing and a sprinkling of coriander.

142

fruity tapioca puddings

SERVES 6

**PREP: 5 MINUTES,
PLUS THAWING AND
COOLING TIME**

COOK: 30 MINUTES

250g mixed frozen berries
3 tbsp caster sugar
100g dried tapioca
650ml semi-skimmed milk
250ml water
2 tsp vanilla extract

**If you like rice pudding desserts, you are bound to love these
creamy tapioca puddings. Tapioca is made from the starch
of a root vegetable that looks a bit like a yam, and when
simmered with milk and vanilla, it makes a comforting dessert
with an intriguing texture. You can find tapioca with pudding
rice in the desserts section of larger supermarkets.**

Put the frozen berries in a freezer bag and add 2 tablespoons
of the caster sugar. Thaw at room temperature for 1–2 hours
until softened and juicy.

Put the tapioca in a large non-stick saucepan and stir in 500ml
of the milk and all the water. Place over a low heat and bring
to a gentle simmer. Cook gently for about 25 minutes, stirring
frequently, until the tapioca is translucent and the sauce
creamy. Stir in the remaining sugar and the vanilla extract.
Take off the heat and stir in the remaining 150ml cold milk
and leave to cool. (The tapioca can also be eaten warm
with cold berries if you prefer.)

Stir the tapioca well and add a little extra water if it's still
a little gluey. Divide between six small dishes and top with
the juicy berries. Eat the same day or up to a day later if
you add the berries just before serving. Cover and keep
chilled in the fridge.

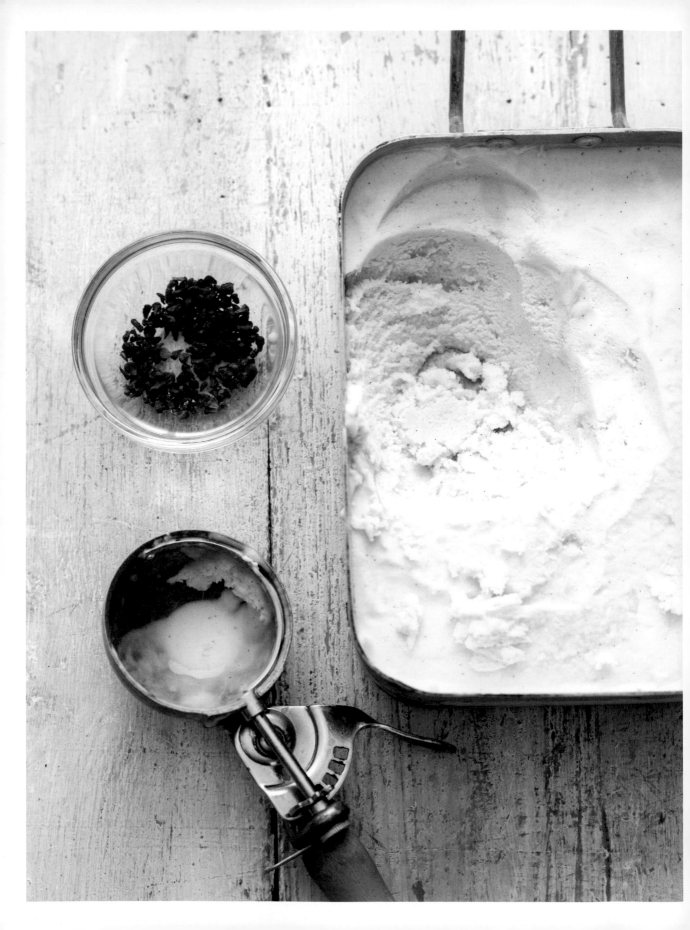

130
CALORIES
PER SERVING

lower-fat vanilla ice cream

SERVES 8

**PREP: 15 MINUTES,
PLUS CHILLING AND
CHURNING TIME**

COOK: 10–12 MINUTES

6 medium egg yolks
50g golden syrup
1 tbsp cornflour
2 tsp vanilla extract
   or vanilla bean paste
150ml single cream
450ml semi-skimmed milk
freeze-dried strawberry
   or raspberry pieces
   to serve (optional)

Tip: If the custard begins
to look grainy as it heats,
it's a sure sign that the eggs
are scrambling, so take it
off the heat immediately
and cool quickly.

Finding reduced-fat ice cream that isn't full of artificial additives seems impossible, so I've started making my own. You will need an ice cream maker for this recipe, but borrow from a friend if you don't want to invest in one of your own. My ice cream has roughly 100 calories less per 100 grams than a shop-bought premium ice cream.

Whisk the egg yolks, syrup, cornflour and vanilla in a medium non-stick saucepan using a silicone covered whisk for 1 minute. Pour the cream and milk into the same pan. (If you don't have a silicone whisk, whisk the egg yolks in a bowl and then transfer to the the saucepan.)

Place over a very low heat and cook for roughly 10–12 minutes, stirring continuously with a wooden spoon, until the custard is beginning to thicken enough to coat the back of the spoon. It's important to make sure the mixture does not overheat otherwise the eggs will begin to scramble (see tip).

Remove the pan from the heat and dunk the base of the saucepan into a sink filled with about 6cm of cold water. This will stop the custard continuing to cook. Stir continuously for 5 minutes, then leave to cool in the cold water for a further 30–45 minutes until cold, stirring occasionally.

Put the cooled custard into a pre-chilled ice cream maker. Churn until very thick then transfer to a freezer-proof container, cover and freeze until solid. It could take over 40 minutes to get to an extremely thick consistency, which is what is needed to help ensure the ice cream scoops easily when served.

Remove from the freezer and leave to stand at room temperature for around 10 minutes before serving. Sprinkle with freeze-dried berries if you like.

frying pan
and griddle

377 CALORIES
PER SERVING

chicken and vegetable frying pan pie

SERVES 4

PREP: 10 MINUTES

COOK: 25–30 MINUTES

25g butter
2 tsp sunflower oil
1 medium onion, finely chopped
400g skinless, boneless chicken breasts (about 3 small), cut into roughly 2cm chunks
25g plain flour
200ml semi-skimmed milk
150ml hot chicken stock (made with ½ chicken cube)
400g frozen mixed vegetables, such as broccoli, peas, carrots and cauliflower
3 sheets of filo pastry (each about 45g)
oil, for spraying or brushing
flaked sea salt
ground black pepper

Tip: If you don't have an ovenproof frying pan, transfer the chicken mixture to a shallow ovenproof dish and top with the pastry. Bake for an extra 5 minutes or until the filling is piping hot. Size and shape of filo pastry can vary, but as long as it covers the top of the pie in loosely crumpled heaps the recipe will work perfectly. Your calories may vary slightly depending on the weight of the pastry.

After an exhausting day at work or running around after the family, this is the sort of dish that means you can sit down and relax, knowing there will be very little washing up at the end of it.

Preheat the oven to 200°C/Fan 180°C/Gas 6. Melt the butter with the sunflower oil in a large, deep ovenproof non-stick frying pan and fry the onion and chicken for 5 minutes over a medium heat until lightly coloured all over, stirring frequently.

Stir in the flour and cook for a few seconds. Slowly add the milk to the pan, stirring continuously, then add the stock and frozen vegetables. Bring to a simmer and cook for 3 minutes, stirring frequently. Season to taste with salt and pepper.

While the chicken and vegetables are cooking, cut each sheet of filo pastry into three pieces, spray or brush lightly with oil and loosely crumple them into small heaps.

Take the pan off the hob and, working quickly, place the crumpled pastry on top of the chicken mixture. Place in the oven and bake for 15–20 minutes, or until the pastry is crisp and golden brown. Take care when you remove the pie as the pan handle will be extremely hot.

351
CALORIES
PER SERVING

italian chicken with mascarpone

SERVES 2
PREP: 5 MINUTES
COOK: 25 MINUTES

2 boneless, skinless chicken
    breasts (each about 150g),
    cut in half horizontally to
    make 4 pieces
1 tbsp sunflower oil
½ medium onion, thinly sliced
2 garlic cloves, crushed
    or finely grated
227g can chopped tomatoes
2 tbsp tomato purée
300ml chicken stock (made
    with ½ chicken cube)
50ml Martini Rosso or
    Madeira (or red wine
    and 1 tsp caster sugar)
1 tsp dried oregano
¼ tsp dried chilli flakes
    (optional)
50g light mascarpone cheese
    (30% less fat)
small handful of fresh basil,
    leaves shredded if large
flaked sea salt
ground black pepper

Freeze the cooked and
cooled chicken without
the mascarpone or basil
in a freezer-proof container
for up to 3 months. Thaw
overnight in the fridge then
transfer to a suitable dish
and microwave on high for
about 5 minutes. Stir well,
top with mascarpone and
microwave for a further
30 seconds or until piping
hot. Garnish with basil.

If you are watching your weight, serve this robust Italian-style dish without additional potatoes, pasta or rice, accompanied by a large mixed salad. It's ready in under 30 minutes and is simple to double up if you are cooking for more than two – or make extra and freeze for another day. If you can't find reduced-fat mascarpone, use the full-fat kind and add an extra 49 calories per serving. Or top with half-fat crème fraiche (24 calories per tablespoon) instead.

Season the chicken breast pieces on all sides with salt and pepper.

Heat the oil in a medium non-stick frying pan (with a base roughly 19cm in diameter). Fry the chicken over a medium-high heat for 3 minutes on each side or until nicely browned and just cooked. Transfer to a plate and set aside.

Add the onion to the pan, reduce the heat and cook for 3 minutes, stirring continuously, until the onion is lightly browned. Stir in the garlic and cook for a few seconds more. (Do not allow the garlic to burn or it will make the sauce taste bitter.)

Tip the tomatoes into the pan, stir in the tomato purée, chicken stock, Martini or Madeira, oregano and chilli flakes, if using. Bring the sauce to a gentle simmer and cook for 10 minutes, stirring frequently.

Place the chicken breasts back into the pan and simmer gently in the hot sauce for 3 minutes. Spoon the mascarpone on top and cook, without stirring, for a further 2 minutes or until the chicken is piping hot and cooked throughout. Remove from the heat and scatter over the basil leaves. Serve with a large mixed salad.

329
CALORIES
PER SERVING

pan-fried pesto chicken

SERVES 2
PREP: 10 MINUTES
COOK: 16–18 MINUTES

2 boneless, skinless chicken
  breasts (each about
  150g), cut in half
  horizontally to make
  4 pieces
½ tsp dried thyme
¼ tsp dried rosemary
½ tsp flaked sea salt
oil, for spraying or brushing
1 medium red onion,
  cut into 10 wedges
1 red pepper, deseeded
  and cut into roughly
  3cm chunks
1 medium courgette, halved
  lengthways and cut into
  roughly 1.5cm slices
1 tbsp pine nuts
20g Parmesan cheese,
  thinly shaved with a
  vegetable peeler
large handful of fresh basil,
  leaves shredded if large
2 tbsp thick balsamic
  vinegar
ground black pepper

I love fresh pesto sauce, but it is usually made with heaps of olive oil, high-fat pine nuts and Parmesan cheese. For this dish, I've included lots of the same flavours but given them a low-calorie twist. If you cut the chicken breasts into four pieces, they cook more quickly and make a serving look very generous.

Sprinkle the chicken breast pieces with the thyme, rosemary, salt and plenty of freshly ground black pepper.

Place a large non-stick frying pan over a medium-high heat. Lightly spray or brush with the oil, add the chicken pieces and fry for 3–5 minutes on each side, until nicely browned and just cooked (there should be no pinkness remaining in the centre when the chicken is cut). Transfer to a plate, cover loosely with foil, and set aside.

Return the pan to the heat, spray or brush with more oil and add the onion wedges, pepper and courgette slices. Stir-fry for 5–7 minutes, or until the vegetables are softened and lightly browned. Add the pine nuts and cook for a minute more, or until lightly toasted.

Return the chicken to the pan and heat through for 1–2 minutes, until hot throughout. Take the pan off the heat and scatter with the Parmesan cheese and basil. Season with black pepper and drizzle with the balsamic vinegar just before serving.

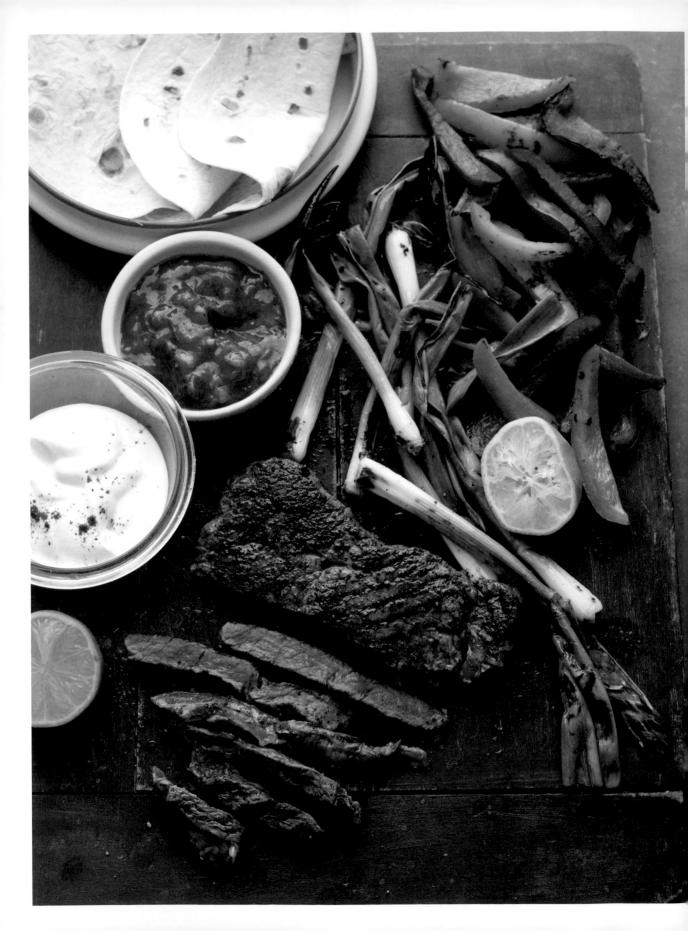

483

smoky steak fajitas

SERVES 2
PREP: 10 MINUTES
COOK: 7-8 MINUTES

250g lean frying steak
(about 1.5cm thick),
trimmed of any hard
fat and sinew
2 tsp sunflower oil
1 yellow pepper,
deseeded and sliced
1 red pepper, deseeded
and sliced
8 spring onions, trimmed
4 x 30g mini flour tortillas
4 tbsp soured cream
4 tbsp ready-made
tomato salsa
lime wedges, for
squeezing (optional)

FOR THE RUB
1 tsp jerk seasoning
½ fine sea salt
½ tsp coarsely ground
black pepper

Tips: If you can't find jerk
seasoning, mix ½ teaspoon
hot smoked paprika and
½ teaspoon ground coriander
instead. It won't be quite
the same, but it will still
taste great.

Make your own salsa by
mixing chopped tomatoes
with finely chopped red
onion, finely diced green
chilli and freshly chopped
coriander leaves.

Have everything ready before you begin cooking the steak,
and put your extractor fan on full blast. You will need to
cook the meat on a high heat for an authentic over-the-coals
flavour. Frying steaks tend to be cheaper and leaner than
prime cuts and are best cooked rare to medium. Look out
for mini flour tortillas – they are just 30g each and contain
around 80 calories rather than 180 calories for a large one.

First, make the rub. Mix together the jerk seasoning, salt and
pepper. Rub the steak all over with half the oil and then the
seasoning mix.

Heat a large non-stick ridged griddle pan over a high heat and
cook the steak for 1½ minutes on each side, until well browned
but not cooked through. Transfer to a board, cover with a piece
of foil and a clean folded tea towel to keep it warm and leave to
rest while you cook the vegetables. (If your steak is thicker than
1.5cm, you will need to increase the cooking time by 30 seconds
or more on each side.)

Return the pan to the heat, add the remaining oil and cook the
peppers and spring onions for about 4 minutes over a medium-
high heat, turning occasionally with tongs until softened and
lightly browned. Transfer to the board.

Meanwhile, heat the tortillas according to the packet instructions.
(Alternatively, heat them on the griddle for a few seconds on
each side.)

Serve the steak and vegetables from the board, piling them
high into warm tortillas with the spring onions and peppers,
soured cream and salsa, with lime wedges on the side if
you like.

352
CALORIES
PER SERVING

tortilla chilli pie

SERVES 5
PREP: 10 MINUTES
COOK: 45 MINUTES

500g lean minced beef
  (10% fat or less)
1 large onion, finely
  chopped
½ tsp hot chilli powder
1 tsp smoked paprika
1 tsp ground cumin
1 tsp ground coriander
150ml red wine or beef stock
500ml beef stock (made
  with 1 beef cube)
400g can chopped
  tomatoes with herbs
2 tbsp tomato purée
400g can red kidney beans,
  drained and rinsed
flaked sea salt
ground black pepper

FOR THE TOPPING
50g plain tortilla chips
50g sliced jalapeño chillies
  (from a jar), drained and
  roughly chopped
  (optional)
50g reduced-fat Cheddar
  cheese, coarsely grated
fat-free fromage frais and
  chopped fresh coriander
  (optional)

Flat-freeze the cooked and
cooled untopped chilli for
up to 3 months. Reheat
from frozen in a large non-
stick flameproof frying pan,
adding a little extra water if
necessary, until piping hot.
Continue as per the recipe.

For this recipe I've made a lower-fat chilli con carne then topped it with tortilla chips, jalapeño chillies and grated cheese. A quick blast under the grill and it's ready to serve alongside a large mixed salad. If you don't have an ovenproof frying pan you can transfer the mince mixture to a pie dish before topping and grilling.

Place a large ovenproof non-stick frying pan over a medium heat and add the beef and onion. Cook together for 3–5 minutes, stirring and squishing the beef against the sides of the pan to break up the mince.

Add the chilli powder, paprika, cumin and coriander. Fry together for 1 minute, then add the wine followed by the stock. Tip the tomatoes into the pan and stir in the tomato purée. Season with salt and plenty of freshly ground black pepper.

Bring to the boil then reduce the heat, cover loosely and simmer gently for 30 minutes, stirring occasionally. Stir in the red kidney beans, return to a gentle simmer and cook uncovered for a further 10 minutes or until the mince is tender and the sauce is thick, stirring frequently.

Preheat the grill to its hottest setting. Take the pan off the heat and scatter the tortilla chips on top of the chilli, then sprinkle with the jalapeños (if using) and cheese.

Place under the grill for 1–2 minutes, or until the cheese melts. Serve topped with fat-free fromage frais and chopped coriander, if you like, and a large mixed leaf salad.

496

moussaka for two

SERVES 2

PREP: 10 MINUTES

COOK: 28-30 MINUTES

1 medium aubergine
(about 250g), cut into
roughly 2cm chunks
oil, for spraying or brushing
250g lamb mince
(20% fat or less)
½ medium onion,
finely chopped
2 garlic cloves, crushed
1 tsp dried oregano
½ tsp dried mint
1 bay leaf
2 tsp plain flour
50ml red wine or extra
lamb stock
200ml lamb stock (made
with ½ lamb cube)
227g can chopped
tomatoes
2 tbsp tomato purée
70g feta cheese, drained,
and broken into small
chunks
small handful of fresh
mint leaves
flaked sea salt
ground black pepper
large mixed leaf salad,
to serve

Flat-freeze the cooked and
cooled moussaka without
the feta cheese and mint.
Reheat from frozen with an
extra 100ml water in a large
non-stick frying pan for
about 20 minutes, stirring
frequently, until piping hot.
Top with the feta and mint.

I like this quick one pan dish of well-seasoned lamb
and aubergine better than a traditional baked moussaka.
The flavours are rich but fresh-tasting, and the dish looks
lovely brought straight to the table. Serve with a large
mixed leaf salad.

Put the aubergine chunks in a medium, non-stick frying
pan – it should have a base roughly 19cm in diameter and
be about 4cm deep – and spray or brush generously with
oil. Season with salt and black pepper and place the pan
over a high heat. Stir-fry for 3–5 minutes, or until the
aubergine is nicely browned but not cooked through.
Tip into a medium bowl and set aside.

Put the minced lamb, onion, garlic, oregano, dried mint
and bay leaf in the pan used to fry the aubergine and cook
over a medium heat for 5 minutes, stirring and squishing
the meat against the side of the pan with a wooden spoon
to break up the mince.

Stir in the flour and season with salt and plenty of freshly
ground black pepper. Pour over the wine, add the lamb
stock, tomatoes and tomato purée. Bring to a simmer
and cook for 10 minutes, stirring occasionally. Return the
aubergine pieces to the pan and cook for a further 5–10
minutes, or until the lamb is tender, the aubergine is soft
and the sauce is thick, stirring occasionally.

Drop the feta chunks on top. Cook for a further 1–2 minutes
without stirring, until the feta begins to melt. Scatter over
the mint leaves and serve with a large mixed leaf salad.

498

CALORIES
PER SERVING

salmon with puy lentils

SERVES 2

PREP: 10 MINUTES

COOK: 25 MINUTES

1 tbsp sunflower oil
2 x 125g salmon fillets
½ medium onion,
    finely chopped
1 celery stick, trimmed
    and thinly sliced
2 small carrots, peeled
    and thinly sliced
50ml white wine
450ml chicken stock (made
    with ½ chicken cube)
250g pouch ready-to-eat
    Puy lentils
10g bunch of fresh flat-leaf
    parsley, leaves roughly
    chopped, plus extra
    to garnish
1 tbsp freshly squeezed
    lemon juice
flaked sea salt
ground black pepper

Tip: The salmon is ready
when the flesh begins to
flake and looks opaque.
Try not to overcook it
or it will become dry.

Sachets of cooked lentils are handy for one pot meals such
as this salmon, cooked with a splash of wine and vegetables.
If you aren't keen on fish, use 2 x 125g lean gammon steaks
instead and the meal will contain 446 calories per serving.

Pour one teaspoon of oil into a large non-stick frying pan and
place over a medium heat. Season the salmon with ground
black pepper and fry for 2 minutes skin-side up, until lightly
browned. Transfer to a plate and set aside.

Heat the remaining oil in the same pan and gently fry the onion,
celery and carrot for 3 minutes, stirring frequently. Stir in the
white wine and chicken stock and bring to a gentle simmer.
Cook for 10 minutes, or until the carrots are just tender,
stirring occasionally.

Stir the lentils and chopped parsley into the pan with the
vegetables and season with the lemon juice, a little salt
and plenty of ground black pepper.

Place the part-cooked salmon on top of the vegetables and
lentils, skin-side down, and simmer for 8–10 minutes, or until
the salmon is just cooked. Stir the lentils occasionally and add
a little extra water if they become dry. Divide the lentils and
vegetables between deep plates, and place the salmon on top
(discarding the salmon skin). Garnish with extra parsley just
before serving.

371
CALORIES
PER SERVING

spanish omelette

SERVES 3
PREP: 10 MINUTES,
PLUS STANDING
COOK: 20–25 MINUTES

1 tbsp olive oil
1 medium onion,
    finely chopped
1 small red pepper,
    deseeded and
    thinly sliced
1 small yellow pepper,
    deseeded and thinly
    sliced
50g soft cooking chorizo,
    cut into 5mm slices
300g can new potatoes,
    drained and thickly sliced
1 garlic clove, crushed
6 medium eggs, beaten
15g bunch of fresh flat-leaf
    parsley, leaves
    finely chopped
flaked sea salt
ground black pepper

It's easy to be a bit sniffy about canned potatoes, but I find them hugely useful for adding to one pot dishes. Here they are combined with lightly sautéed vegetables, chorizo and beaten eggs for an almost authentic Spanish omelette. Serve warm or cold and if you want to make a vegetarian version, simply leave out the chorizo.

Heat the oil in a medium, flameproof non-stick frying pan with a base roughly 19cm in diameter. Add the onion and peppers and cook for 10 minutes over a medium heat until softened and beginning to colour, stirring occasionally.

Add the chorizo and potatoes to the frying pan, season well with salt and plenty of freshly ground black pepper and cook for a further 3 minutes or until hot, stirring frequently. Add the garlic and cook for a few seconds more, stirring.

Mix the beaten eggs and parsley, season with salt and pepper and pour over the vegetables and chorizo. Cook for 5 minutes over a low-medium heat without stirring. Preheat the grill to a medium-hot setting. Place the frying pan under the grill and cook for a further 4–5 minutes or until the eggs are set.

Leave to stand for 5 minutes, then loosen the edges of the omelette with a heatproof palette knife – not metal as it could scratch the non-stick coating – and turn out onto a board. Serve warm in wedges with a large salad. Alternatively, leave to cool then pack into a container, cover and keep in the fridge. Eat within 2 days.

499
CALORIES
PER SERVING

warm griddled halloumi salad

SERVES 2
PREP: 10 MINUTES
COOK: 16 MINUTES

1 tsp sunflower oil
1 red pepper, deseeded
 and cut into roughly
 3cm chunks
1 yellow or orange pepper,
 deseeded and cut into
 roughly 3cm chunks
1 medium courgette,
 cut into roughly 1.5cm
 diagonal slices
1 medium red onion,
 cut into 8 wedges
 with the root intact
½ long red chilli, finely
 chopped (deseeded
 first if you like)
1 tbsp extra virgin olive oil
1 tsp fresh lemon juice
227g halloumi cheese,
 cut into 8 slices
small handful of rocket
 leaves and fresh
 mint leaves
ground black pepper

Halloumi is a semi-firm Cypriot cheese that can be sliced and grilled without melting too much. Its salty taste and firm texture means that it is ideally suited to this summery salad.

Place a large, ridged non-stick griddle pan over a high heat for about 5 minutes or until very hot. Put the sunflower oil in a bowl and add the prepared vegetables. Toss gently together.

Griddle the vegetables, in batches if necessary, for about 10 minutes or until softened and lightly browned, turning occasionally. Put in a serving dish or platter and toss with the chilli, olive oil and lemon juice. Season with lots of ground black pepper.

Put the sliced halloumi on the griddle and cook for ½ –1 minute on each side until hot and lightly charred, turning with a spatula or palette knife. Arrange in the dish with the vegetables. Scatter over the rocket and mint leaves and serve while warm.

120
CALORIES
PER SERVING

caribbean pineapple

SERVES 4
PREP: 15 MINUTES
COOK: 15–20 MINUTES

1 ripe medium pineapple
    (about 1.2kg)
2 tsp sunflower oil
fresh juice of 2 limes
    (about 4 tbsp)
3 tbsp soft light
    brown sugar
15g butter
finely pared zest of
    ½ lime (optional)

Pineapple makes a lovely hot pudding, especially when served with my low-fat banana 'ice cream'. Make sure you cook the pineapple long enough for it to start caramelising in the pan – that way, you don't need to add too much sugar. The calorie count here is for the pineapple only.

Put the pineapple on a board and cut off the top and bottom. Next, cut off all the thick skin and cut out any prickly 'eyes'. Cut the pineapple in half lengthways and then cut each half into 6–8 long slices and cut out the tough central core.

Heat 1 teaspoon of the oil in a large non-stick frying pan and fry half the pineapple slices for 3–4 minutes on each side over a medium-high heat until hot and lightly browned.

Transfer to a plate then add the remaining oil and pineapple to the pan and cook in exactly the same way. Transfer to the same plate as the first batch and return the pan to the heat.

Add the lime juice, butter and sugar to the pan and cook for 1–2 minutes, stirring continuously, until the sugar dissolves and the sauce becomes syrupy. Return the pineapple to the pan and heat through for 1–2 minutes, turning it in the hot sauce.

Divide the hot pineapple and sauce between plates and sprinkle with finely pared or grated lime zest, if you like. Serve with scoops of low-fat banana 'ice cream' (see below). Alternatively, a dribble of chilled single cream goes well, but you'll need to add an extra 29 calories for each tablespoon.

Low-fat banana 'ice cream': Peel 3 ripe medium bananas and cut into thick slices. Scatter over a baking tray and freeze until solid. Tip into the bowl of a sturdy food processor or blender and add 100g fat-free natural yoghurt. Blitz until smooth and thickly iced (it's best to use a food processor or blender designed to crush ice). Serve immediately or scrape into a freezer-proof container and return to the freezer for 3–4 hours until firm. Stand at room temperature for a few minutes before serving. Serves 6. Calories per serving: 56

ovenproof dish

420
CALORIES
PER SERVING

baked chicken and mushroom risotto

SERVES 4
PREP: 15 MINUTES
COOK: 1 HOUR

10g dried porcini
   mushrooms
250ml just-boiled water
1 medium onion, finely
   chopped
250g closed-cup
   mushrooms, sliced
2 garlic cloves, very
   thinly sliced
oil, for spraying or brushing
3 small boneless, skinless
   chicken breasts (about
   450g total weight), cut
   into roughly 2cm chunks
200g Arborio (risotto) rice
100ml Madeira or
   extra stock
350ml hot chicken stock
   (made with 1 chicken
   cube)
50g Parmesan or Grana
   Padano cheese,
   finely grated
flaked sea salt
ground black pepper
fresh flat-leaf parsley,
   roughly chopped,
   to garnish (optional)
large mixed salad, to serve

Tip: If you notice a little grit at the bottom of your mushroom soaking water, simply strain the liquid through a fine muslin or brand new kitchen cloth before using.

This full-flavoured risotto is quick to assemble and can be left to cook in the oven, so you don't need to stand stirring it for ages. The dried mushrooms give it a rich, luxurious taste; you will find them in larger supermarkets. Serve this dish with a large mixed salad.

Preheat the oven to 200°C/Fan 180°C/Gas 6. Put the dried mushrooms in a measuring jug and add the water. Leave to stand for about 20 minutes.

Meanwhile, put the onion, fresh mushrooms and garlic in a 3 litre shallow ovenproof dish – a lasagne dish is ideal. Spray or brush with oil and season with salt and plenty of black pepper. Cook in the oven for 15 minutes until softened.

Strain and roughly chop the dried mushrooms, reserving the soaking water. Take the baking dish out of the oven and add the chicken, rice, Madeira or stock, soaked chopped mushrooms and their liquor. Pour over the chicken stock, stir well and cover the dish tightly with foil. Return to the oven for 30 minutes.

Take the dish out of the oven, remove the foil and stir. Cover and return to the oven for a further 10 minutes, or until most of the liquid has been absorbed and the rice is tender. Remove the foil once more, stir in the grated cheese and adjust the seasoning to taste. Scatter with chopped parsley if you like. Serve with a large mixed salad.

416
CALORIES
PER SERVING

couscous with roasted roots, honey and goat's cheese

SERVES 2
PREP: 10 MINUTES
COOK: 35 MINUTES

2 parsnips (each about 150g), peeled and cut into short batons, about 1.5cm wide and 3–4cm long

2 carrots (each about 100g), peeled and cut into short batons, about 1.5cm wide and 2–3cm long

1 tbsp olive oil

1 tbsp clear honey

¼–½ tsp dried chilli flakes (adjust quantity depending on taste)

125ml hot vegetable or chicken stock (made with ½ vegetable or chicken cube)

75g dried, uncooked couscous

1 tbsp fresh lemon juice

20g bunch of fresh flat-leaf parsley, leaves roughly chopped

100g cooked beetroot, drained and cut into wedges

50g soft, rindless goat's cheese, cut into small pieces

flaked sea salt

ground black pepper

Tip: It's best to use vacuum packed beetroot without vinegar for this recipe (you'll find it with the salad ingredients in the supermarket) but beetroot from a jar can be used too.

A colourful and filling salad with lots of lovely flavours. I like it served warm, but it's also great for packed lunches and will serve four people as an accompaniment.

Preheat the oven to 200°C/Fan 180°C/Gas 6. Scatter the parsnips and carrots over the base of a small, shallow ovenproof dish – it will need to hold about 1 litre – and drizzle with the olive oil. Season with a little salt and lots of ground black pepper and roast for 20 minutes.

Take the dish out of the oven, drizzle the vegetables with the honey and sprinkle with the chilli flakes. Turn to lightly coat, then return to the oven for a further 10 minutes, or until golden and sticky. Tip into a heatproof bowl and set aside.

Pour the vegetable or chicken stock into the ovenproof dish and stir in the couscous. Cover with foil and return the dish to the oven for 5 minutes. Remove the foil, sprinkle over the lemon juice and most of the parsley and fluff up with a fork. Season with salt and pepper. Return the cooked vegetables to the dish and toss together with the couscous.

Scatter the beetroot and goat's cheese on top. Garnish with the reserved parsley and serve warm.

273

spiced lamb-stuffed courgettes

SERVES 4
PREP: 15 MINUTES
COOK: 50 MINUTES

4 medium courgettes
(each about 200g),
cut in half lengthways
and seeds scooped
out with teaspoon
oil, for spraying or
brushing 250g minced
lamb (20% fat or less)
75g bulgur wheat
(uncooked)
1 small red pepper,
deseeded and cut into
roughly 1.5cm chunks
6 sun-dried tomato
pieces, drained and
finely chopped
1 medium onion, very
finely chopped
2 garlic cloves, crushed
or finely grated
2 tbsp harissa paste
(preferably rose harissa)
1 tsp ground cumin
1 tsp ground coriander
finely grated zest and
juice of 1 lemon
20g bunch of fresh
mint, leaves
finely chopped, plus
extra to garnish
150ml hot lamb stock
(made with ½ lamb cube)
4 tbsp fat-free natural
yoghurt
1 tbsp pomegranate
molasses or thick
balsamic vinegar
ground black pepper
flaked sea salt

These courgettes are stuffed with minced lamb, spices and bulgur wheat. When baked with a little stock, the wheat softens and expands, making a really delicious supper dish that's great served straight from the oven with spoonfuls of natural yoghurt and a drizzle of pomegranate molasses or thick balsamic vinegar. If you can buy 10% fat lean minced lamb you will save about 51 calories per portion.

Preheat the oven to 220°C/Fan 200°C/Gas 7. Place the halved courgettes fairly tightly together, cut-side up, in a single layer in a shallow ovenproof dish or baking tray. Spray or brush with a little oil, season with salt and pepper and bake for 20 minutes.

To make the stuffing, mix the lamb, bulgur wheat, red pepper, tomato, onion, garlic, harissa, spices, lemon zest and juice, chopped mint leaves and stock. Season with lots of freshly ground black pepper and a little salt.

Take the courgettes out of the oven and spoon the stuffing loosely into the cavities. Cover the dish with foil and bake for 20 minutes. Remove the foil and cook for a further 10 minutes or until the courgettes are softened and the topping is golden and tender. Spoon over the yoghurt, scatter with extra mint leaves and drizzle over the pomegranate molasses or thick balsamic vinegar. Serve hot with a large mixed salad.

254
CALORIES
PER SERVING

salmon and asparagus crustless quiche

SERVES 4

PREP: 10 MINUTES, PLUS COOLING TIME

COOK: 45 MINUTES

oil, for spraying or brushing
2 fresh salmon fillets
    (each about 125g)
250g asparagus spears
    (not too thick),
    trimmed and halved
2 spring onions, trimmed
    and thinly sliced
20g cornflour
1 tbsp semi-skimmed milk
3 large eggs
200g half-fat crème fraiche
10g bunch of fresh dill,
    leaves roughly chopped
flaked sea salt
ground black pepper

Tip: Use a ceramic quiche dish for this recipe if you like – it should be about 22cm in diameter and about 4cm high.

Making a quiche without a pastry crust may seem a little odd, but it works well and drastically reduces the calories. Serve in wedges with a mixed salad if you like.

Preheat the oven to 200°C/Fan 180°C/Gas 6. Spray or brush a shallow round ceramic pie dish with oil and place the salmon fillets in it, skin-side down and at least 5cm apart.

Scatter the asparagus and spring onions around the salmon and season with black pepper. Spray or brush with a little more oil and cover the dish with foil. Bake for 12–15 minutes, or until the salmon is just cooked and flakes easily when prodded with a fork.

Take the dish out of the oven and turn the fish over. Remove the skin and flake the fish into large pieces with a couple of forks. Make sure that the fish, spring onions and asparagus are evenly distributed. Reduce the oven temperature to 180°C/Fan 160°C/Gas 4.

Mix the cornflour and milk in a bowl until smooth, then add the eggs, one at a time, and beat together well. (If lumps remain, use a whisk rather than a wooden spoon.) Stir in the crème fraiche and dill. Season well with salt and pepper.

Pour the egg mixture over the salmon and bake for about 30 minutes, or until just set. Leave to cool for at least 15 minutes before cutting into wedges to serve.

416
CALORIES
PER SERVING

spanish baked fish with chorizo

SERVES 2
PREP: 10 MINUTES
COOK: 30 MINUTES

1 orange or yellow pepper, deseeded and cut into roughly 3cm chunks
1 medium red onion, peeled and cut into thin wedges
1 medium courgette, trimmed and cut into roughly 1.5cm slices
oil, for spraying or brushing
1 small lemon
50g soft cooking chorizo, cut into 5mm slices
2 x 150g skinless thick white fish fillets, such as cod, haddock or pollack
200g cherry tomatoes, on the vine if possible
good pinch smoked paprika
1 tbsp extra virgin olive oil
400g can butter beans, drained and rinsed
flaked sea salt
ground black pepper

A lovely, lightly-spiced cod dish that's perfect if you aren't a confident cook but want to try your hand at cooking fish. It's low in calories but has heaps of flavour and is very filling thanks to all the vegetables and beans. The combination of fish and spicy Spanish sausage works particularly well.

Preheat the oven to 220°C/Fan 200°C/Gas 7. Put the pepper, onion and courgette in a shallow ovenproof dish, spray or brush with a little oil, season with salt and black pepper and bake for 15 minutes.

Cut the lemon in half and cut each half into four chunks. Take the vegetables out of the oven and stir in the chorizo and half the lemon pieces. Place the fish and tomatoes on top of the vegetables.

Squeeze the remaining lemon chunks over the top. Season the fish with salt and pepper and sprinkle with paprika.

Return to the oven and bake for 12 minutes. Take the dish out of the oven and carefully stir the beans into the vegetables and chorizo without disturbing the fish too much.

Return to the oven for a further 5 minutes, or until the beans are hot and the fish is just cooked (this will depend on thickness of the fillets). Serve with a lightly dressed green salad.

104

CALORIES
PER HALF PEPPER

chinese rice-stuffed peppers

MAKES 6
PREP: 10 MINUTES
COOK: 1 HOUR

3 large red peppers
1 large egg
1 yellow or orange pepper, deseeded and diced
150g button mushrooms, thinly sliced
50g frozen peas
6 spring onions, trimmed and thinly sliced
2 garlic cloves, crushed or finely grated
150g cold cooked long grain rice (from a sachet or home-cooked)
2 tbsp dark soy sauce, plus extra to serve
½ tsp dried chilli flakes
flaked sea salt
freshly ground black pepper

A simple, vegetable-packed dish with Chinese flavours. Serve half a pepper with a large mixed salad for a light supper, or two halves for a more filling meal.

Preheat the oven to 200°C/Fan 180°C/Gas 6. Cut the red peppers in half from stem to base and scoop out all the seeds. Place in a single layer, cut side up, in a shallow ovenproof dish – a lasagne dish is ideal. Cut a thin sliver off the base of any peppers that don't sit flat so they hold the filling without tipping. Bake for 20 minutes.

Beat the egg in a medium bowl and stir in the diced yellow or orange pepper, mushrooms, peas, spring onions and garlic. Add the rice, soy sauce and chilli flakes and season with salt and pepper and stir until combined.

Pile the rice mixture into the peppers, cover the dish tightly with foil and bake for 40 minutes, or until piping hot. Serve with more soy sauce for drizzling.

208
CALORIES
PER SERVING

easy baked apples

SERVES 4
PREP: 5 MINUTES
COOK: 30 MINUTES

100g mixed dried fruit
20g flaked almonds
finely grated zest of 1 lemon
3 medium Bramley cooking
   apples (each about 275g)
3 tbsp fresh lemon juice
1 tbsp maple syrup or
   clear honey
25g butter
fat-free fromage frais or
   half-fat crème fraiche,
   to serve

Tip: If you want to cut
the calories further, leave
out the butter and save
46 calories per serving.
If the apples begin to
scorch before they are
completely soft, simply
cover the dish with foil
and continue baking.

Baked apples make a great low-calorie pudding, but unless you have an apple corer and spare time for stuffing, they can be a bit of a hassle. My recipe simply cuts the apples into quarters and bakes them on top of mixed dried fruit and flaked almonds. It's much quicker and, I think, more delicious.

Preheat the oven to 200°C/Fan 180°C/Gas 6. Mix the dried fruit, flaked almonds and lemon zest in a small ovenproof dish with a base roughly 21cm in diameter.

Cut the apples into quarters and remove the cores. Place the apples on top of the dried fruit. The apple pieces should sit in a single layer, skin-side up and cover the dried fruit so it doesn't burn.

Drizzle with the lemon juice and maple syrup or honey, dot with butter and bake uncovered for 30 minutes, or until the apples are very tender. Serve with fat-free fromage frais or half-fat crème fraiche, but don't forget to add the extra calories.

251 CALORIES PER SERVING

nectarine and blueberry muffin cobbler

SERVES 6
PREP: 10 MINUTES
COOK: 35 MINUTES

4 firm ripe nectarines
(about 450g total weight)
150g fresh blueberries

FOR THE TOPPING
50g caster sugar
50ml semi-skimmed milk
1 tsp vanilla extract
50g unsalted butter,
well softened
2 medium eggs
150g self-raising flour
1 tsp baking powder

Tip: Peaches make a great alternative to nectarines and contain a similar number of calories. Prepare them in exactly the same way as the nectarines.

When we first made this in the test kitchen, we thought it tasted just like a warm blueberry muffin – hence the name! The light, fluffy topping is perfect with the juicy nectarines and blueberries. Mix the batter ingredients in a freezer bag to cut down on the washing up.

Take a nectarine and, holding it carefully, cut out slices from top to bottom towards the stone with a small knife, working your way around the whole fruit. Drop the slices into a shallow ovenproof dish, which holds roughly 1.75 litres. You should end up with roughly 8 slices. Discard the stone.

Slice the remaining fruit. Toss the slices with half the blueberries. Preheat the oven to 190°C/Fan 170°C/Gas 5.

To make the topping, put the caster sugar in a large, thick zip-seal freezer bag and add the milk, vanilla extract, butter, eggs, flour and baking powder. Seal the bag and mix the ingredients, squishing and pressing together from outside the bag until thoroughly combined. This will take 2–3 minutes. (You can also mix the ingredients in a food processor or a bowl with a spoon or an electric whisk until smooth.)

Add the rest of the blueberries and mix until lightly combined. Squeeze the open bag over the nectarines, and cover them roughly with the cake batter. Spread it to the sides but don't worry if there are a few gaps.

Bake for 35 minutes, or until the fruit is tender and the topping is risen and golden brown. Serve warm with low-fat custard, half-fat crème fraiche or single cream, but don't forget to add the extra calories.

173
CALORIES
PER SERVING

quick-mix banana and sultana cake

SERVES 12
PREP: 10 MINUTES
COOK: 1–1¼ HOURS

oil, for spraying or brushing
3 very ripe bananas (about
    300g peeled weight)
3 medium eggs
1 tsp ground mixed spice
5 tbsp sunflower oil
15g soft light brown sugar
250g self-raising flour
1 tsp baking powder
50g sultanas

Freeze the cooked and cooled cake wrapped in foil, and placed in a large freezer bag for up to 1 month. Unwrap and thaw at room temperature for about 3 hours before serving.

Tip: Make sure you use a strong, thick freezer bag to mix the ingredients or the plastic could split. You can also combine the cake ingredients in a bowl with an electric whisk until thick and then add the sultanas.

You can mix the batter for this simple cake in a freezer bag to save time and washing up! Choose naturally sweet overripe bananas for the best results.

Preheat the oven to 180°C/Fan 160°C/Gas 4. Line the base and sides of a 20cm springclip cake tin with baking parchment and lightly grease with a little oil.

Peel the bananas and cut them into short lengths. Put them in a large, thick freezer bag and squish and press the outside of the bag with your hands until the bananas are mushy.

Add the eggs, mixed spice, sunflower oil, sugar, flour and baking powder and continue to squash, squish and press until you have a thick, almost smooth batter. This will take 4–5 minutes. Add the sultanas and mix until just combined.

Open the bag and squeeze the cake batter into the prepared tin. Bake for 1–1¼ hours, or until a skewer inserted into the centre of the cake comes out clean. Leave the cake to cool in the tin, then remove and peel off the parchment. Cut into thin wedges to serve.

casserole

321
CALORIES
PER SERVING

tarragon chicken

SERVES 4
PREP: 15 MINUTES
COOK: 30–35 MINUTES

400g boneless, skinless
    chicken breast mini fillets
20g butter
1 tsp sunflower oil
1 small onion, finely
    chopped
1 garlic clove, finely
    chopped
100ml white wine
500ml chicken stock (made
    with ½ chicken cube)
300g new potatoes, such
    as Charlotte, cut into
    1cm slices
300g small carrots, such
    as Chantenay, scrubbed
    or peeled and halved
    lengthways if thick
small bunch (roughly 15g)
    of fresh tarragon
250g slender asparagus
    spears, trimmed
    and halved
3 tbsp double cream
flaked sea salt
ground black pepper

Chicken breasts and colourful vegetables are cooked in a light tarragon-infused sauce. I use chicken mini fillets as they're quite cheap, are easy to cook and require no preparation, but you could use sliced boneless chicken breasts instead.

Season the chicken fillets all over with a little flaked sea salt and plenty of freshly ground black pepper. Melt the butter with the oil in a large, shallow flameproof casserole or non-stick sauté pan and fry the chicken fillets for 2–3 minutes on each side over a medium-high heat until golden brown and cooked through. Transfer to a plate and set aside.

Add the onion and garlic to the pan and cook for 2–3 minutes, stirring frequently until the onion is softened and beginning to colour. (Take care not to let the garlic burn or it will taste bitter.) Pour the wine into the pan and let it bubble furiously for a few seconds, then stir in the stock, potatoes, carrots and 2 tarragon sprigs. Cover the pan loosely and simmer very gently for 15 minutes, or until the potatoes are just cooked.

Increase the heat and add the asparagus to the pan. Bring the cooking liquor to the boil and cook the asparagus for about 5 minutes or until almost tender. While the asparagus is cooking, strip the leaves from the remaining tarragon sprigs and chop them roughly.

Stir the cream and chopped tarragon into the sauce and simmer for a further 2 minutes, stirring occasionally. Return the chicken to the pan and heat through for 1–2 minutes or until completely hot throughout. Season to taste and serve immediately.

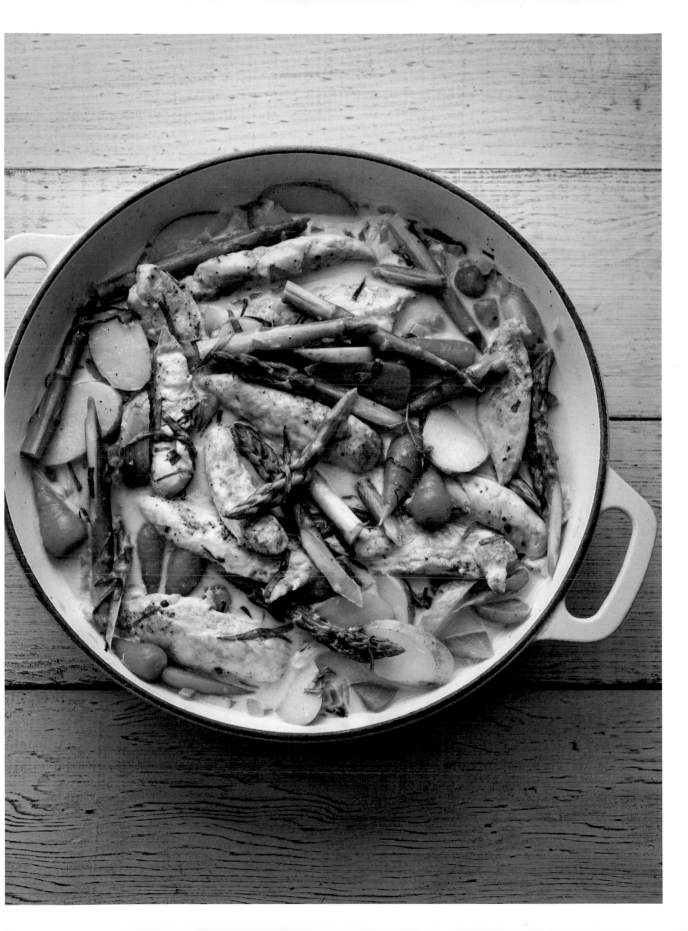

480

simple cassoulet

SERVES 5
PREP: 15 MINUTES
COOK: 1 HOUR

oil, for spraying or brushing
6 herby sausages (at least
    85% meat)
1 medium onion,
    thinly sliced
2 garlic cloves, crushed
    or finely grated
2 lean smoked back bacon
    rashers, cut into roughly
    1.5cm slices
6 boneless, skinless chicken
    thighs (about 500g),
    trimmed of visible fat
    and cut into three
3 celery sticks, trimmed
    and cut into roughly
    2cm diagonal slices
3 medium carrots, peeled
    and cut into roughly
    2cm diagonal slices
400g can chopped tomatoes
150ml red wine or water
300ml chicken stock (made
    with 1 chicken cube)
½ tsp dried chilli flakes
1 bay leaf
400g can cannellini or kidney
    beans, drained and rinsed
400g can butter beans,
    drained and rinsed
150g baby spring greens
    or kale, trimmed and
    thickly shredded
flaked sea salt
ground black pepper

This is one of those dishes that everyone seems to like.
It's a simple combination of tender chicken thighs and
sausages in a rich tomato sauce with canned beans and
vegetables – perfect for a weekend lunch, but easy enough
for a mid-week supper too.

Spray or brush a large flameproof casserole with oil. Add
the sausages to the pan and cook over a medium heat for
10 minutes, turning occasionally until browned on all sides.
Take the sausages out of the casserole and put them on
a board.

Preheat the oven to 200°C/Fan 180°C/Gas 6. Add the onion
to the casserole and cook for 5 minutes, stirring frequently
until softened and lightly browned. Add the garlic, bacon
and chicken pieces to the pan with the onions and cook for
3–5 minutes, turning the chicken twice until very lightly
coloured all over.

Cut the sausages into three pieces and return them to the pan,
with the celery, carrots, chopped tomatoes, red wine or water
and stock. Stir in the chilli flakes and bay leaf and season with
a little salt and lots of ground black pepper. Bring to a simmer
on the hob then cover and transfer to the oven. Cook for
20 minutes.

Take the casserole out of the oven and stir in all the beans.
Cover again and return to the oven for a further 15 minutes.
Transfer the casserole to the hob and stir in the spring greens
or kale. Bring to a simmer and cook for a further 3–5 minutes
or until the greens are tender, stirring frequently.

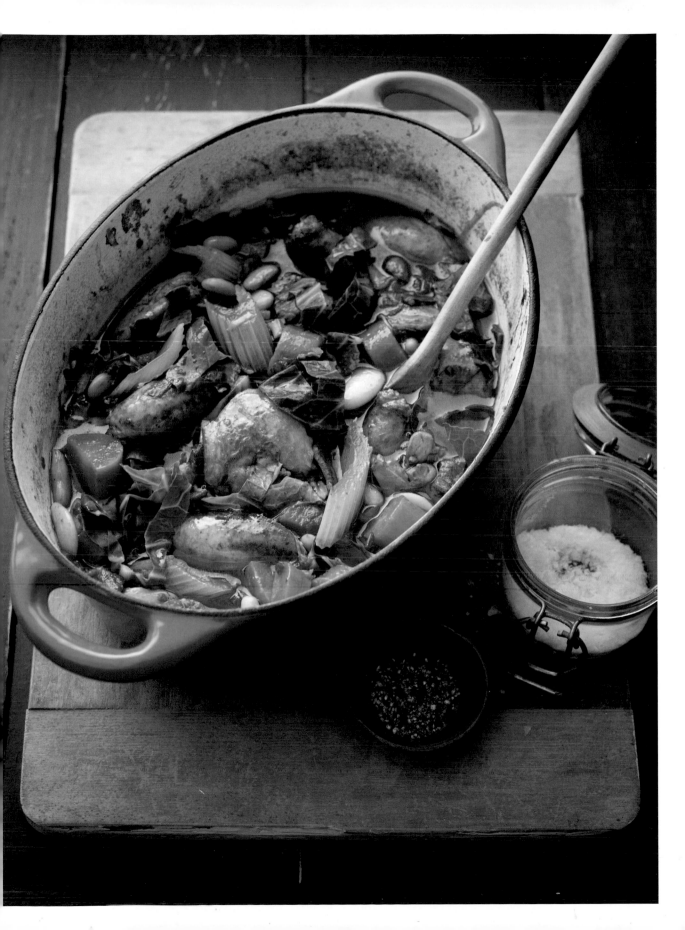

445

oven-baked chicken and prawn paella

SERVES 5
**PREP: 15 MINUTES,
PLUS SOAKING TIME**
COOK: 35 MINUTES

generous pinch of
   saffron threads
250ml just-boiled water
1 medium onion,
   finely chopped
1 red pepper, deseeded
   and cut into roughly
   3cm chunks
1 green pepper, deseeded
   and cut into roughly
   3cm chunks
oil, for spraying or brushing
6 boneless, skinless chicken
   thighs (about 500g),
   trimmed of visible fat
   and cut in half
100g soft cooking chorizo,
   cut into 5mm slices
250g Arborio (risotto) rice
2 garlic cloves, crushed
   or finely grated
2 tsp hot smoked paprika
100ml dry sherry
   or extra stock
500ml hot chicken stock
   (made with 1 chicken cube)
250g cooked, peeled king
   prawns, thawed if frozen
15g bunch of fresh flat-leaf
   parsley, leaves roughly
   chopped
flaked sea salt
ground black pepper

Tip: You can use any sherry;
but 100ml of sweet sherry
or Madeira contains about
20 calories more than
dry sherry.

A wide-based, fairly shallow casserole works best for this recipe, which is great if you are a bit nervous about cooking rice. I've kept things simple and because the paella is baked in the oven, you should have perfect results every time.

Preheat the oven to 200°C/Fan 180°C/Gas 6. Put the saffron in a measuring jug and add the just-boiled water. Leave to stand for about 10 minutes.

Put the onion and peppers in a shallow flameproof casserole, which holds roughly 2.5 litres. Spray or brush with oil and season with salt and lots of ground black pepper. Fry over a medium heat for 5 minutes, stirring frequently.

Stir in the chicken and chorizo and cook for a further 3 minutes, stirring. Add the rice, garlic, paprika, sherry or stock, plus the saffron and its soaking liquor. Pour over the chicken stock and bring to a simmer. Cover with a lid and cook in the oven for 20 minutes.

Take out of the oven, remove the lid and stir in the prawns and parsley. Cover and return to the oven for a further 5 minutes, or until the prawns are heated through and the rice is tender.

382
CALORIES
PER SERVING

all-in-one beef and ale stew

1 tbsp sunflower oil
1 medium onion,
   thinly sliced
4 tbsp plain flour
1 tsp flaked sea salt
2 tsp dried mixed herbs
800kg lean braising beef
   (ideally chuck steak),
   trimmed of hard fat
   and cut into 3cm cubes
1 bay leaf
500ml bottle real ale
350ml beef stock (made
   with 1 beef cube)
2 tbsp tomato purée
2 tsp caster sugar
5 medium carrots (each
   about 100g), peeled
   and cut into roughly
   2cm slices
2 parsnips (each about
   150g), peeled, halved
   lengthways and cut
   into roughly 2cm chunks
500g medium potatoes
   (ideally Maris Piper),
   peeled and cut into
   roughly 3cm chunks
100g fine green beans,
   trimmed and halved
ground black pepper

Freeze the cooled stew in a freezer-proof container for up to 2 months. Thaw overnight in the fridge then reheat in the microwave or an ovenproof casserole in a preheated oven at 200°C/Fan 180°C/Gas 6 for 45–60 minutes, stirring after 30 minutes, until piping hot.

The large quantity of vegetables in this stew helps you keep the meat to a minimum. Buy good braising beef – the kind you cut yourself rather than pre-diced – if you can. If you don't want to use beer, add 500ml more beef stock instead or half beef stock and half red wine. Made with 500ml extra stock, the stew will contain about 357 calories per serving; made with 250ml stock and 250ml red wine, it will contain about 386 calories per serving.

Preheat the oven to 180°C/Fan 160°C/Gas 4. Heat the oil in a large flameproof casserole. Fry the onion over a medium-high heat for about 5 minutes until lightly browned, stirring frequently. Remove from the heat.

Put the flour, salt and dried herbs in a large, sturdy freezer bag. Season with lots of freshly ground black pepper. Toss the meat in the flour until coated evenly all over. Tip the meat into the pan with the onions.

Add the bay leaf, ale, stock, tomato purée and sugar. Stir well and bring to the boil. Cover and carefully transfer to the oven. Cook for 1¼ hours. Take the casserole out of the oven, remove the lid and stir in the carrots, parsnips and potatoes. Cover and return to the oven for a further hour, or until the beef is tender.

Stir in the green beans, cover and return to the oven for a further 15 minutes, or until the beans are tender. Adjust the seasoning to taste before serving.

430
CALORIES
PER SERVING

chinese braised beef with noodles

SERVES 5
PREP: 15 MINUTES
COOK: 2³/4 HOURS

1 tbsp sunflower oil
2 medium onions,
    thinly sliced
1kg braising beef (ideally
    chuck steak), trimmed
    of hard fat and sinew
    and cut into roughly
    4cm chunks
50g chunk of fresh root
    ginger, peeled and
    finely grated
4 garlic cloves, finely grated
1 tsp dried chilli flakes
2 tsp Chinese five
    spice powder
750ml hot beef stock
    (made with 1 beef cube)
4 tbsp dark soy sauce
2 tbsp clear honey
2 medium-large carrots,
    peeled and cut into
    roughly 1cm diagonal
    slices
4 tsp cornflour
1 tbsp cold water
250g pouch ready-cooked
    medium noodles
3 small pak choi, quartered
    lengthways
ground black pepper

Good-quality braising beef is cooked with Chinese spices, soy sauce and honey until meltingly tender. Cooked noodles and pak choi are added towards the end of the cooking time to make a fabulous one-pot dish. Sprinkle with sliced spring onions or a mixture of finely chopped red chillis and peanuts just before serving. Peanuts contain about 150 calories per 25g.

Preheat the oven to 180°C/Fan 160°C/Gas 4. Heat the oil in a large, wide-based flameproof casserole. Fry the onions and beef over a medium-high heat for 10 minutes, or until lightly browned, stirring frequently.

Add the ginger and garlic and cook for a further 2 minutes, stirring. Sprinkle over the chilli and five spice powder and season with lots of ground black pepper. Cook for 1 minute, stirring.

Pour the beef stock, soy sauce and honey into the casserole and stir well. Bring to a simmer, cover and carefully transfer to the oven. Cook for 1½ hours. Add the carrots and cook for 30–45 minutes more or until the beef is very tender.

Take the casserole out of the oven. Increase the oven temperature to 220°C/Fan 200°C/Gas 7. Mix the cornflour with the water until smooth. Stir the noodles and cornflour mixture into the beef, place the pak choi on top, cover and return to the oven for a further 15 minutes or until the pak choi is tender and the noodles are hot.

411 CALORIES PER SERVING

one-pot beef curry

SERVES 6
PREP: 10 MINUTES
COOK: 2 HOURS

1 tbsp sunflower oil
2 medium onions,
    finely chopped
2 garlic cloves, crushed
4 tbsp medium curry paste
1.2kg good quality braising
    beef (ideally chuck steak),
    trimmed of hard fat and
    sinew and cut into
    roughly 3cm chunks
1 tsp flaked sea salt
2 x 400g cans chopped
    tomatoes
200ml beef stock (made
    with 1 beef cube)
400g potatoes (ideally
    Maris Piper), peeled
    and cut into roughly
    4cm chunks
3 medium carrots (about
    300g), peeled and cut
    into 2cm diagonal slices
150g young spinach leaves

Freeze the cooked and
cooled curry in labelled zip-
seal bags or foil containers
for up to 2 months. Thaw
overnight in the fridge then
reheat in the microwave or
a wide-based saucepan
over a medium heat, stirring
occasionally until piping hot.

This one-pot beef curry is very easy to make. I save time by using a ready-made medium curry paste – you can choose a mild or hot paste if you prefer. Serve with generous spoonfuls of minted cucumber raita (see below).

Preheat the oven to 180°C/Fan 160°C/Gas 4. Heat the oil in a large, flameproof casserole and fry the onion and garlic over a high heat for 1 minute, stirring. Add the curry paste and cook for a few seconds, stirring well.

Add the beef and salt to the pan and cook for 3 minutes, turning the beef regularly until lightly coloured and well coated in the spice paste. Tip the tomatoes into the pan and stir in the beef stock.

Bring the liquid to a simmer, then cover and transfer carefully to the oven. Cook for 1 hour. Take the casserole out of the oven and stir in the potatoes and carrots. Return to the oven for a further hour, or until the beef is beautifully tender and the sauce has thickened.

Place the casserole carefully on the hob and stir in the spinach, just a handful at a time, until softened. Adjust the seasoning to taste and serve with minted cucumber raita, if you like.

Easy minted cucumber raita: Cut half a cucumber into small chunks, put in a small bowl and season with a little flaked sea salt. Stir in 200g fat-free natural yoghurt, 2 teaspoons mint sauce (from a jar) and 1 teaspoon caster sugar. Leave to stand for 10 minutes before serving. Serves 6. Calories per serving: 26

432

CALORIES
PER SERVING

pibil pulled pork tacos

SERVES 6
PREP: 10 MINUTES,
PLUS MARINATING TIME
COOK: 3 HOURS

1kg boned pork shoulder,
   trimmed of rind and fat
   and cut into 4 large
   chunks (snip off the
   string and unroll first
   if necessary)
1 medium red onion,
   roughly chopped
175ml cold water
12 corn tacos, warmed
1 little gem lettuce, trimmed
   and finely shredded
soured cream or half-fat
   crème fraiche, and lime
   wedges to serve

FOR THE MARINADE
3 tbsp chipotle chilli paste
   (from a jar)
3 tbsp white wine vinegar
   or cider vinegar
2 tsp dried oregano
1 tsp ground allspice
1 tsp ground cumin
1 tsp flaked sea salt
½ tsp ground cloves
½ tsp ground black pepper

Tip: Heat the tacos on
a baking tray in the oven
for a few minutes once the
pork has been removed.

This isn't a truly authentic Mexican pibil pork recipe, but
it's easy to put together with ingredients from the supermarket,
and I reckon it tastes pretty close to the original. Soft, succulent
and spicy, it's fantastic piled into warm tacos with homemade
gently pickled onion (see below), shredded lettuce and soured
cream (add 31 calories per tablespoon).

Put all the marinade ingredients in a large, sturdy freezer
bag and squish them around until well combined. Add the
pork and onion and move around in the bag until they are well
coated with the marinade. Seal and put in the fridge overnight.

The next day, transfer the pork and its marinade to a small
casserole and stir in the cold water. Cover and place in the
oven. Set the temperature to 170°C/Fan 150°C/Gas 3 and
cook the pork for 3 hours, or until it is so tender that it
falls apart when poked with a fork.

Remove the casserole from the oven and shred the meat with
two forks. Serve the pulled pork from the casserole or a board
with warm corn tacos, shredded lettuce, pickled red onion and
soured cream or crème fraiche (but don't forget to add the
extra calories), and a squeeze of fresh lime.

Pickled red onion: Finely slice a red onion and put it in a
heatproof bowl. Cover with just-boiled water and leave to stand
for 10 minutes. Drain well and then stir in 2 tablespoons of white
wine vinegar or cider vinegar and 1 teaspoon of caster sugar
and stand for at least 10 minutes before serving. Serves 6.
Calories per serving: 13

415 CALORIES PER SERVING

moroccan lamb tagine

SERVES 6
PREP: 15 MINUTES
COOK: 1½ HOURS

800g lamb neck fillet,
    trimmed of hard fat and
    cut into 4cm chunks
4 tsp ras-el-hanout
    spice mix
1 tsp cumin seeds
2 medium onions, halved
    and thinly sliced
oil, for spraying or brushing
4 garlic cloves, thinly sliced
750ml hot lamb stock
    (made with 1 lamb cube)
2 x 400g cans chopped
    tomatoes
4 tsp harissa paste
    (preferably rose harissa)
2 tbsp clear honey
400g can chickpeas,
    drained and rinsed
300g sweet potato, peeled
    and cut into roughly
    3cm chunks
20g bunch of fresh
    coriander, leaves finely
    chopped, plus extra
    to garnish
flaked sea salt
ground black pepper

Flat-freeze the cooked and
cooled casserole in two
large labelled zip-seal bags
for up to 2 months. Thaw
overnight in the fridge then
reheat in the microwave or
a wide-based saucepan,
stirring occasionally until
piping hot.

Lamb tagine always seems to go down well and this simplified version has all the ingredients for a most welcome one pot. There's no need to serve with additional carbohydrates, but you may want to add couscous or rice for anyone not watching their weight. If you don't have ras-el-hanout, mix 2 teaspoons of ground coriander, 2 teaspoons ground cumin, 1 teaspoon ground ginger and ¼ teaspoon ground cinnamon instead.

Put the lamb in a large, flameproof casserole and season all over with salt and pepper, the ras-el-hanout and cumin seeds. Add the sliced onions and toss together well.

Preheat the oven to 200°C/Fan 180°C/Gas 6. Spray or brush the seasoned lamb and onions with oil and cook over a medium-high heat for about 10 minutes, or until lightly coloured all over, stirring and turning the meat and onions frequently.

Add the garlic and cook for a further 2 minutes, stirring. Pour over the lamb stock, then tip the tomatoes into the pan, add the harissa and honey and bring to a gentle simmer. Cover and cook in the oven for 30 minutes.

Take the casserole out of the oven and stir in the chickpeas and sweet potato. Cover and return to the oven for a further 45 minutes, or until the lamb is very tender. Sprinkle with chopped coriander and serve with a lightly dressed green salad.

305
CALORIES
PER SERVING

one-pan fish pie

SERVES 4

PREP: 10 MINUTES

COOK: 30-35 MINUTES

20g butter
2 medium leeks (each about 175g), trimmed and cut into roughly 1cm slices
½ small onion, finely chopped
400ml semi-skimmed milk
4 tbsp cornflour
4 tbsp cold water
400g frozen mixed fish for pies
100g frozen cooked, peeled king prawns
flaked sea salt
ground black pepper

FOR THE TOPPING
300g can new potatoes, drained
10g butter

Tip: Packs of frozen mixed fish pieces, containing a mixture of white fish, salmon and smoked fish, are brilliant for this recipe as the fish can be cooked from frozen – often packs of larger prawns can be reheated from frozen too. If you are using thawed or fresh fish, you will need to reduce the cooking time by roughly 5 minutes.

If you haven't cooked much fish before but fancy trying your hand at a fish pie, this recipe is a great place to start. I've simplified the traditional method and cut the calories to create a dish that's very simple to make and bake.

Preheat the oven to 220°C/Fan 200°C/Gas 7. Melt the butter over a low heat in a small flameproof casserole with a base roughly 23cm in diameter. Add the leeks and onion and cook for 5 minutes or until well softened, stirring frequently.

Pour the milk into the pan and bring to a gentle simmer. Mix the cornflour and water into a smooth paste in a small bowl, then pour into the warm milk. Return to a simmer and cook over a low heat for 2–3 minutes, until the sauce is smooth and very thick, stirring continuously. Season well.

Stir the frozen fish pieces and prawns into the sauce and cook for 2 minutes, stirring gently. Remove from the heat. Coarsely grate the potatoes and scatter over the fish mixture then dot with the butter.

Season with a little ground black pepper and bake uncovered for 20–25 minutes, or until the fish and prawns are hot throughout and the topping is golden.

90
CALORIES
PER SERVING

mulled pears

SERVES 5
PREP: 10 MINUTES
COOK: 30 MINUTES

1 tbsp cornflour
150ml red wine
50ml cold water
50g caster sugar
1 cinnamon stick
2 star anise
1 large orange
4 firm but ripe
   Conference pears
half-fat crème fraiche or
   single cream, to serve

Freeze the cooked and cooled pears in their sauce in a freezer-proof container for up to 1 month. Thaw overnight in the fridge and serve cold or heat gently in the microwave or a wide-based saucepan over a low heat until hot.

Make the most of pears when they are plentiful and poach them in lightly-spiced red wine. You needn't buy expensive wine for this recipe; just use a bottle of cheap plonk and freeze what's left over to liven up a meaty casserole or gravy another day. Add 24 calories per tablespoon for half-fat crème fraiche and 29 for single cream.

Preheat the oven to 190°C/Fan 170°C/Gas 5. Put the cornflour into a medium casserole and stir in 2 tablespoons of the wine until smooth, then add 50ml water, the sugar, cinnamon stick and star anise.

Using a potato peeler, peel the orange in large, wide strips and add them to the pan. Squeeze the orange juice and add to the pan.

Peel the pears and cut them into quarters lengthways. Remove the cores with the tip of a knife. Drop the pear quarters into the wine mixture and place over a medium heat.

Bring the liquid to a simmer, turning the pears a couple of times, then cover the casserole and cook the pears in the oven for 30 minutes, or until just tender. You can test a couple with the tip of a knife.

Serve warm or leave to cool. Place in the fridge until ready to serve (up to 2 days). Serve topped with a little single cream or half-fat crème fraiche.

bowl and
platter

324

chicken, quinoa, avocado and chilli salad

SERVES 6
PREP: 20 MINUTES
COOK: 12 MINUTES

150g uncooked quinoa
875g cold cooked roast
  chicken (from the
  chiller cabinet)
400g can red kidney beans,
  rinsed and drained
200g cherry tomatoes,
  halved
40g bunch of coriander,
  leaves roughly chopped
4 spring onions, thinly sliced
1 long red chilli, finely
  chopped (deseeded
  first if you like)
1 firm but ripe avocado,
  stoned, peeled and sliced

FOR THE DRESSING
fresh juice of 2 limes
  (about 3 tbsp lime juice)
1 tbsp chipotle paste
  (from a jar)
1 garlic clove, crushed
  or finely grated
1 tbsp sunflower or olive oil
fine sea salt
ground black pepper

The smoky flavour of the dressing for this salad comes from chipotle paste, made from smoked jalapeño peppers. You can find it in the Mexican section of larger supermarkets. Alternatively, add 1 teaspoon of hot smoked paprika to the dressing. Quinoa is a highly nutritious South American seed that can be served in a similar way to rice.

Half fill a medium saucepan with water and bring to the boil. Rinse the quinoa in a fine sieve then add to the water, stir well and simmer for about 12 minutes, or until just tender. It is ready when it begins to shed the c-shaped outer husks.

While the quinoa is cooking, put the chicken on a board and strip off all the meat, discarding the skin and bones. Tear or cut the meat into chunky pieces and put to the side.

Rinse the cooked quinoa in a sieve under cold water, then press hard with a ladle or serving spoon to remove as much of the excess water as possible.

Mix the dressing ingredients in a large bowl. Tip in the quinoa and toss with the dressing ingredients, kidney beans, tomatoes, coriander, spring onions and chilli. Season well with salt and pepper. It's important to make sure that the dressing is mixed well through the salad.

Add the chicken and avocado to the salad and toss everything gently together before serving.

359

CALORIES
PER SERVING

satay chicken wraps

SERVES 2

PREP: 10 MINUTES

2 cooked boneless,
  skinless chicken breasts
  (200g pack)
2 little gem lettuces,
  leaves separated, rinsed
  and drained
4 spring onions, cut into
  very fine matchsticks
⅓ cucumber, cut into
  very fine matchsticks
1 medium carrot, peeled
  and cut into very
  fine matchsticks
1 small red pepper,
  deseeded and cut into
  very fine matchsticks
fresh coriander leaves,
  to garnish (optional)
lime wedges, to serve
  (optional)

FOR THE PEANUT SAUCE
2 tbsp crunchy peanut
  butter
3 tbsp just-boiled water
1 tbsp Thai sweet chilli
  dipping sauce
1 tbsp dark soy sauce

A brilliant informal supper dish that's easy to prepare and fun to eat. It also makes a great packed lunch, arranged in a lidded container and taken to work.

To make the peanut sauce, put the peanut butter in a small bowl and stir in the just-boiled water until smooth. Add the chilli sauce and soy sauce and mix well.

Cut the chicken breasts into thin slices and put on a large platter. Put the lettuce leaves, spring onions, cucumber, carrot and red pepper in separate piles beside the chicken.

Take the chicken and salad to the table and serve by putting slices of chicken into lettuce leaves and topping with the shredded vegetables and the peanut sauce. Garnish with fresh coriander and serve with extra lime wedges for squeezing over the wraps, if you like.

277
CALORIES
PER SERVING

avocado on toast

SERVES 2
PREP: 5 MINUTES
COOK: 2 MINUTES

4 small slices of wholegrain
bread (each slice
about 30g)
1 ripe avocado (about 145g)
2 tsp thick balsamic vinegar
ground black pepper

There is something intensely satisfying about perfectly ripe avocado served on hot toast with a drizzle of balsamic vinegar. It's full of good fats and makes a great light lunch or snack – it beats a cheese sarnie any day.

Toast the bread on both sides and divide the slices between plates. Cut the avocado in half and remove the stone.

Scoop out the flesh and put on a board. Slice the avocado and arrange the slices on the hot toast, mashing them into the toast a little with a knife, then drizzle with the balsamic vinegar. Season with ground black pepper and serve.

362
CALORIES
PER SERVING

nectarine, prosciutto and mozzarella salad

SERVES 2
PREP: 10 MINUTES

50g bag of rocket leaves
2 firm but ripe nectarines
125g ball of mozzarella,
    drained
5–6 thin slices prosciutto,
    Serrano or Parma ham
    (about 70g pack)
½ long red chilli, deseeded
    and finely chopped
1 tbsp extra virgin olive oil
2 tsp thick balsamic vinegar
ground black pepper

This is a lovely salad to serve outside on a sunny day. You can use peaches instead of nectarines if you like, and reduced-fat mozzarella if you prefer, but I think the full-fat version has a much better texture and flavour for just 32 calories more per serving.

Scatter the rocket leaves over a serving platter. Take a nectarine and, holding it carefully, cut out slices from top to bottom towards the stone with a small knife, working your way around the whole fruit. You should get 8–10 slices from each nectarine. Discard the stones.

Arrange the nectarine slices on the platter with the rocket leaves and tear the mozzarella on top. Add the prosciutto, torn into wide strips. Sprinkle with the chopped chilli and drizzle with the olive oil and balsamic vinegar. Season with ground black pepper and serve.

176
CALORIES
PER SERVING

giant prawn cocktail

SERVES 4
PREP: 10 MINUTES

1 romaine lettuce,
   leaves separated
4 medium tomatoes,
   quartered
½ cucumber, thinly sliced
350g cooked, peeled
   prawns, thawed if frozen
   and drained well
pinch of paprika
chopped fresh dill,
   to garnish (optional)
ground black pepper
lemon wedges, to serve

FOR THE DRESSING
4 tbsp light mayonnaise
2 tbsp fat-free fromage frais
3 tbsp tomato ketchup

Tip: Use smaller cold-water
Atlantic prawns for the best
results. If you can't get hold
of fat-free fromage frais,
use fat-free yoghurt in the
dressing instead.

I love a prawn cocktail and there's no need to exclude it when you are watching your weight, as I've made the dressing with reduced-fat mayonnaise and fromage frais. This one is made in a large dish, but you can serve it in smaller individual dishes if you prefer. One small slice of wholemeal bread spread with ¼ teaspoon softened butter will add 88 calories to each serving.

To make the dressing, mix the mayonnaise, fromage frais and tomato ketchup in a small bowl.

Arrange the lettuce leaves in a large, wide dish and top with the tomatoes and cucumber. Scatter the prawns on top and spoon over the dressing.

Sprinkle with paprika and ground black pepper. Garnish with fresh dill if you like, and serve immediately with lemon wedges for squeezing and thinly-sliced brown bread.

225
CALORIES
PER SERVING

yoghurt with banana and dates

SERVES 2
PREP: 5 MINUTES

300g fat-free
 Greek yoghurt
1 medium ripe banana
40g dried stoned dates,
 roughly chopped
15g mixed seeds (such
 as pumpkin, sesame
 and sunflower)
2 tsp clear honey (optional)

This yoghurt makes a quick breakfast for busy days. I find the banana and dates sweeten it enough, but you can always add a little honey, too. A teaspoon of honey will increase the calories by 14 per serving.

Divide the yoghurt between two small bowls. Peel and slice the banana and scatter on top. Sprinkle with the dates and seeds and serve drizzled with a little honey, if you like.

Berry yoghurt: Divide 2 x 150g pots of fat-free yoghurt between two bowls. Top with 100g halved, hulled strawberries, 100g raspberries and 50g blueberries. Drizzle with 2 teaspoons clear honey. Serves 2. Calories per serving: 135

60
CALORIES
PER SERVING

apple, melon, pineapple and pomegranate salad

SERVES 8
PREP: 10 MINUTES

1 small ripe pineapple
    (about 950g)
1 small cantaloupe melon
    (about 950g), ideally
    with orange flesh
2 large eating apples
    (each about 200g)
100g pomegranate seeds
150ml fresh orange juice
    (from a carton or freshly
    squeezed from 2 oranges)
fat-free yoghurt, to serve
    (optional)

Tip: Use ready prepared pomegranate seeds from a packet in the chilled fruit section of the supermarket, or buy a large whole pomegranate, remove the seeds yourself and add them and any juice to the salad.

I like to make this crunchy fruit salad for breakfast and as a snack. It keeps really well in the fridge for around 3 days, which means I can grab a bowl first thing in the morning or whenever I'm feeling a bit peckish. Add 8 calories per tablespoon of fat-free yoghurt.

Place the pineapple on a board and carefully cut off the leaves and skin using a large sharp knife. Pick out any prickly eyes with the tip of a knife. Cut the pineapple into quarters lengthways and remove the central core. Cut the flesh into small, chunky pieces and put in a large bowl.

Cut the melon into six wedges and discard the seeds. Cut carefully between the melon skin and flesh in a long sweeping motion, to separate the flesh from the skin. Cut the flesh into small, chunky pieces. Add to the pineapple.

Cut the apples into quarters and remove the cores. Cut the quarters into roughly 2cm chunky pieces. Add to the other fruit. Scatter the pomegranate seeds over the chopped fruit, stir in the orange juice and toss everything together. Cover and chill for about 1 hour before serving (if you can wait) then divide into dessert dishes or tumblers and top with fat-free Greek yoghurt, if you like.

98
CALORIES
PER SERVING

mango, grape and apple salad

SERVES 5
PREP: 10 MINUTES

1 large ripe mango
(about 450g)
2 large eating apples
(each about 200g)
150g green seedless grapes,
washed and drained
150g red seedless grapes,
washed and drained
150ml fresh orange juice
fat-free Greek yoghurt,
to serve (optional)

Tip: If you use freshly squeezed orange juice rather than juice from a carton, you will need 2 large oranges for about 150ml of juice.

A juicy, colourful salad that works well as a pudding, breakfast or snack. The acidity of the orange juice should stop the apples turning brown, so this fruit salad will keep well in the fridge for a couple of days. Add 8 calories per tablespoon of fat-free yoghurt.

Cut the mango in half on either side of the large flat stone. Using a large serving spoon, scoop out the flesh. Cut the mango into small chunks and put in a serving bowl.

Cut the apples into quarters and remove the cores. Cut the quarters into thin slices and add to the mango.

Stir in the grapes, halving any that are particularly large, pour in the orange juice and toss everything together gently. Cover and chill for about 1 hour before serving (if you can wait). Divide into dessert dishes or tumblers and top with fat-free Greek yoghurt, if you like.

little
pots

107
CALORIES
PER SERVING

smoked salmon breakfast muffins

SERVES 6
PREP: 5 MINUTES
COOK: 18 MINUTES

5g softened butter,
  for greasing
6 medium eggs
4 spring onions, trimmed
  and thinly sliced
50g sliced smoked salmon
ground black pepper

Tip: These muffins will keep well in the fridge for a day or two in a sealed container.

These muffins make a protein-rich breakfast or snack that's easy to transport and can be eaten warm or cold. Serve with a mixed salad for a light lunch if you like, too.

Preheat the oven to 200°C/Fan 180°C/Gas 6. Grease and line a 6-hole muffin tin with squares of baking parchment (about 12cm squares).

Beat the eggs in a jug with a large metal whisk until smooth. Season with black pepper and stir in the sliced spring onions.

Cut the salmon slices into thin strips and divide between the holes of the muffin tin. Pour the egg mixture on top.

Bake the muffins for about 18 minutes, or until the egg is slightly risen and only just set on top – it should still be a little soft, as the egg will continue to cook once the tin has been taken out of the oven. Serve warm or cold.

156

smoked mackerel pâté

SERVES 6
PREP: 10 MINUTES

4 smoked mackerel fillets
    (about 225g), skinned
½ small onion
150g quark (fat-free
    soft cheese)
2 tbsp creamed horseradish
    sauce
finely grated zest and juice
    of ½ small lemon
flaked sea salt
ground black pepper
Melba toast and vegetable
    sticks, to serve

Freeze the prepared pâté
in toughened glass jars or
ramekins for up to 1 month.
Thaw overnight in the fridge
and eat within 24 hours.

Tips: Ready-made thin
Melba toasts go well with
this pâté. You'll need to add
about 13 calories for each
toast and make sure you
supplement them with lots
of 'free' vegetables (see
the list on page 181).

If you can't find quark in
your local supermarket,
place 200g fat-free fromage
frais in a muslin-lined sieve
over a bowl and strain it
overnight in the fridge.

Smoked mackerel pâté is easy to whizz together and makes
a simple starter or snack. It's also great for taking to work,
alongside a little bag packed with fresh vegetable sticks.
If you don't have a food processor, mash the ingredients
together with a sturdy fork.

Flake the mackerel into a food processor. Peel the onion and
coarsely grate onto a board. Put the grated onion in one hand
and squeeze it hard over the mackerel to release the juice;
this will add flavour to the pâté. Discard the onion flesh.

Add the quark, horseradish sauce, lemon zest and juice to the
mackerel and season well with a good pinch of salt and plenty
of ground black pepper. Blitz all the ingredients together until
smooth. Adjust the seasoning to taste and add a little more
lemon juice if needed. Spoon the mixture into six small ramekin
dishes or little glass Kilner jars and smooth the surface with
the back of a teaspoon. Cover and chill.

Take the pâté out of the fridge 20 minutes before serving.
Put the ramekins on small plates with Melba toast or vegetable
sticks. Eat within 2 days.

433

tuna and bean layered salad pots

SERVES 2

PREP: 10 MINUTES

200g canned red kidney
beans, drained and rinsed
200g canned cannellini
beans, drained and rinsed
½ small red onion,
thinly sliced
1 medium carrot, peeled
and coarsely grated
8 cherry tomatoes, halved
2 romaine lettuce leaves
or 1 little gem lettuce,
shredded
198g can tuna steak in
spring water, drained
flaked sea salt
ground black pepper

FOR THE DRESSING
1 tsp Dijon mustard
1 tsp caster sugar
1 small garlic clove, crushed
1 tbsp white wine vinegar
4 tbsp olive oil

Tip: Store any unused beans
in a covered container in the
fridge for up to 2 days. Use
for salads, or stir into soups
or stews.

Layered salads are great for packed lunches and picnics.
Make sure the dressing stays at the bottom of the dish and only
mix the salad just before serving, or it could go soggy. Make it
in one large bowl if you are eating at home, or divide between
two sturdy containers or pots if you are taking it to work.

To make the dressing, put all the ingredients in a large bowl,
add a pinch of salt and some black pepper and whisk with
a small metal whisk until slightly thickened.

Add the beans to the bowl and stir in the red onion. (Divide
between two lidded containers if you like.) Place the grated
carrot, tomatoes and shredded lettuce on top, without stirring.

Flake the tuna out of the can and onto the salad with a fork.
Season with pepper. Cover and chill until ready to serve,
then lightly toss all the ingredients together.

92
CALORIES
PER SERVING

swirly lemon yoghurt pots

SERVES 4

PREP: 5 MINUTES

400g fat-free
   Greek yoghurt
3 tbsp lemon curd
100g fresh raspberries
fresh mint leaves and pared
   lemon zest, to decorate
   (optional)

This creamy dessert takes just five minutes to make, but tastes incredibly luxurious – just right when you fancy something sweet, but don't want to wreck your diet.

Put the Greek yoghurt in a bowl and stir until smooth. Add the lemon curd a spoonful at a time and stir it very lightly through the yoghurt. Spoon into glass tumblers or jars and top with fresh raspberries. Decorate with mint leaves and pared lemon zest, if you like.

176
CALORIES
PER SERVING

milk chocolate pots

SERVES 4

PREP: 10 MINUTES, PLUS COOLING AND CHILLING TIME

COOK: 5 MINUTES

100g plain dark chocolate (about 50% cocoa solids)
400g fat-free fromage frais

These simple chocolate puddings are made with melted dark chocolate mixed with fromage frais, so they taste light and creamy.

Break 90g of the chocolate into pieces and place in a large heatproof bowl. Set the bowl over a pan of gently simmering water, making sure the bottom of the bowl isn't in contact with the water, until almost melted. (Alternatively, melt in the microwave.) Carefully remove the bowl from the pan and stir the chocolate with a metal spoon until smooth. Leave to cool for about 30 minutes but do not allow to set.

Stir the fromage frais lightly into the melted chocolate. Don't overmix or it will become too runny. Divide the mixture between ramekins or espresso coffee cups. Grate the reserved 10g chocolate on top.

Place on a small tray, cover and chill for at least 1 hour before serving. Eat within 2 days.

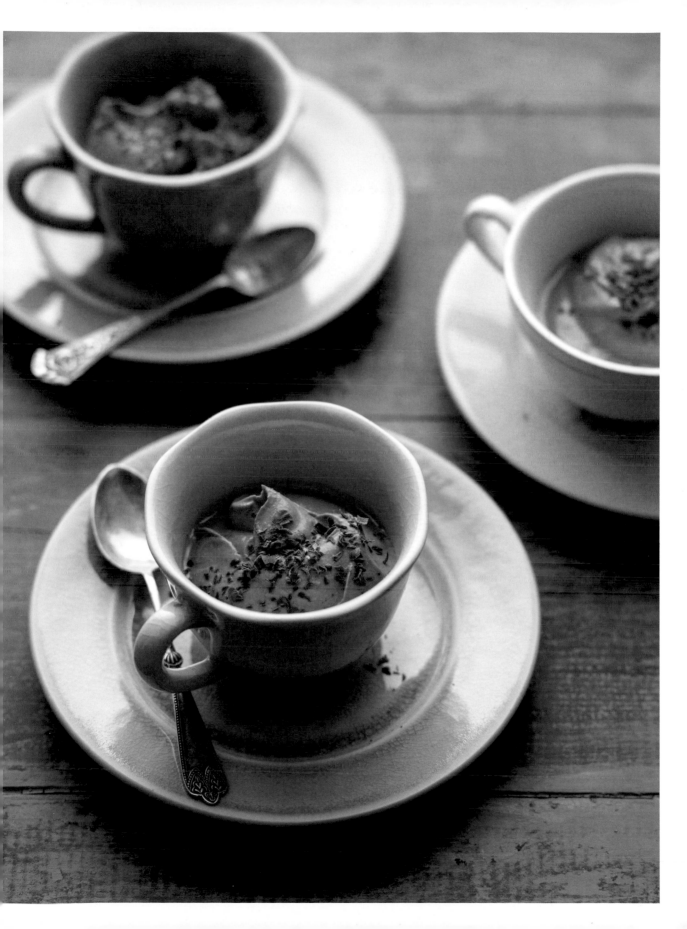

187
CALORIES
PER SERVING

banoffee yoghurt pots

SERVES 4

PREP: 5 MINUTES

3 digestive biscuits

2 medium ripe
  bananas, sliced

400g fat-free Greek
  yoghurt

2 tbsp soft light
  brown sugar

20g tiny fudge pieces
  (from cake decoration
  section at the
  supermarket) or
  dairy fudge, cut
  into small chunks

Banoffee pie is one of my favourite desserts, but is a definite no-no when I'm watching my weight. Here's my low calorie version with all the same elements but given a skinny twist.

Crumble two of the digestive biscuits and divide them between four glasses, dishes or bowls. Top with one of the sliced bananas, spoon over half the yoghurt and sprinkle lightly with half the soft light brown sugar.

Add the remaining banana, yoghurt and brown sugar. Crumble the remaining biscuit on top, sprinkle with tiny fudge pieces and serve.

203
CALORIES
PER SERVING

summer berry crunch pies

SERVES 4
PREP: 10 MINUTES
COOK: 25 MINUTES

500g frozen mixed
   summer berries
1 tbsp cornflour
25g caster sugar
low-fat custard or half-fat
   crème fraiche, to serve
   (optional)

FOR THE TOPPING
25g fridge-cold butter,
   cut into cubes
20g plain flour
75g corn flakes

Frozen berries make a quick and convenient low-calorie pudding and are full of vitamins and fibre. You can use them frozen for this recipe or thaw them first if you like, and take 10 minutes off the cooking time. Serve warm with low-fat custard or half-fat crème fraiche, but don't forget to add the extra calories.

Preheat the oven to 200°C/Fan 180°C/Gas 6. Mix the frozen fruit, cornflour and sugar in a large freezer bag, then divide between individual ovenproof dishes and place them on a baking tray.

To make the topping, put the ingredients into the same bag and rub together between your fingertips outside of the bag until they resemble coarse breadcrumbs. This should take 2–3 minutes.

Scatter the topping mixture evenly over the fruit filling. Bake the pies in the centre of the oven for about 25 minutes, or until the fruit filling is hot throughout and the topping is crisp and golden brown.

159

CALORIES
PER SERVING

strawberry, blackcurrant and banana smoothie

SERVES 4
PREP: 5 MINUTES

450g fresh ripe
    strawberries, hulled
    and halved
1 medium ripe banana
    (roughly 100g peeled
    weight)
3 tbsp blackcurrant cordial
200g fat-free natural
    yoghurt
25g porridge oats
250ml semi-skimmed milk

Tip: If making ahead, pour
the smoothie into lidded
containers and keep in the
fridge. You'll need to add
extra water or milk, as the
oats will continue to thicken
as the smoothie stands.

This vitamin C-rich smoothie is great for a quick breakfast and can be made the night before and kept in the fridge. Transport it to work in a cool bag and shake well before drinking.

Put the strawberries, banana, blackcurrant cordial, yoghurt and oats in a blender or food processor and blitz to a thick purée.

Add half the milk and blitz until as smooth as possible. Add extra milk, a little at a time, until a drinkable consistency is reached. Pour into tall glasses or jars and serve.

a few notes on the recipes

INGREDIENTS

Where possible, choose free-range chicken, meat and eggs. Eggs used in the recipes are medium unless otherwise stated.

All poultry and meat has been trimmed of as much hard or visible fat as possible, although there may be some marbling within the meat. Boneless, skinless chicken breasts weigh about 175g. Fish has been scaled, gutted and pin-boned, and large prawns are deveined. You'll be able to buy most fish and seafood ready prepared but ask your fishmonger if not and they will be happy to help.

PREPARATION

Do as much preparation as possible before you start to cook. Discard any damaged bits, and wipe or wash fresh produce before preparation unless it's going to be peeled.

Onions, garlic and shallots are peeled unless otherwise stated, and vegetables are trimmed. Lemons, limes and oranges should be well washed before the zest is grated. Weigh fresh herbs in a bunch, then trim off the stalks before chopping the leaves. I've used medium-sized vegetables unless stated. As a rule of thumb, a medium-sized onion or potato (such as Maris Piper) weighs about 150g.

All chopped and sliced meat, poultry, fish and vegetable sizes are approximate. Don't worry if your pieces are a bit larger or smaller than indicated, but try to keep roughly to the size so the cooking times are accurate. Even-sized pieces will cook at the same rate, which is especially important for meat and fish.

I love using fresh herbs in my recipes, but you can substitute frozen herbs in most cases. Dried herbs will give a different, more intense flavour, so use them sparingly.

The recipes have been tested using sunflower oil, but you can substitute vegetable, groundnut or mild olive oil. I use dark soy sauce in the test kitchen but it's fine to use light instead – it'll give a milder flavour.

CALORIE COUNTS

Nutritional information does not include the optional serving suggestions. When shopping, you may see calories described as kilocalories on food labels; they are the same thing.

HOW TO FREEZE

Freezing food will save you time and money, and lots of the dishes in this book freeze extremely well. If you don't need all the servings at the same time, freeze the rest for another day. Where there are no instructions for freezing a dish, freezing won't give the best results once reheated.

When freezing food, it's important to cool it rapidly after cooking. Separate what you want to freeze from what you're going to serve and place it in a shallow, freezer-proof container. The shallower the container, the quicker the food will cool (putting it in the freezer while it's still warm will raise the freezer temperature and could affect other foods). Cover loosely, then freeze as soon as it's cool.

If you're freezing a lot of food at once, for example after a bulk cooking session or a big shop, flip the fast freeze button on at least two hours before adding the new dishes and leave it on for twenty-four hours afterwards. This will reduce the temperature of your freezer and help ensure that food is frozen as rapidly as possible.

When freezing food, expel as much air as possible by wrapping it tightly in a freezer bag or foil to help prevent icy patches, freezer burn and discolouration, or flavour transfer between dishes. Liquids expand when frozen, so leave a 4–5cm gap at the top of containers.

If you have a small freezer and need to save space, flat-freeze thick soups, sauces and casseroles in strong zip-seal freezer bags. Fill the bag a third full, then turn it over and flatten it until it is about 1–2cm thick, pressing out as much air as possible and sealing firmly.

Place delicate foods such as breaded chicken or fish fillets and burgers on a tray lined with baking parchment, and freeze in a single layer until solid before placing in containers or freezer bags. This method is called open freezing and helps stop foods sticking together in a block, so you can grab what you need easily.

Label everything clearly, and add the date so you know when to eat it at its best. I aim to use food from the freezer within about four months.

DEFROSTING

For the best results, most foods should be defrosted slowly in the fridge for several hours or overnight. For safety's sake, do not thaw dishes at room temperature.

Flat-frozen foods (see above) will thaw and begin to reheat at almost the same time. Just rinse the bag under hot water and break the mixture into a wide-based pan. Add a dash of water and warm over a low heat until thawed. Increase the heat, adding a little more water if necessary, and simmer until piping hot throughout.

Ensure that any perishable foods that have been frozen are thoroughly cooked or reheated before serving.

HOW TO GET THE BEST RESULTS

Measuring with spoons

Spoon measurements are level unless otherwise stated. Use a set of measuring spoons for the best results; they're endlessly useful, especially if you're watching your sugar, salt or fat intake.

> 1 tsp (1 teaspoon) = 5ml
> 1 dsp (1 dessertspoon) = 10ml
> 1 tbsp (1 tablespoon) = 15ml

A scant measure is just below level and a heaped measure is just above. An Australian tablespoon holds 20ml, so Australian cooks should use 3 level teaspoons instead. See the page opposite for more measurement conversions.

CONVERSION CHARTS

Oven temperature guide

	Electricity °C	Electricity °F	Electricity (fan) °C	Gas Mark
Very cool	110	225	90	$1/4$
	120	250	100	$1/2$
Cool	140	275	120	1
	150	300	130	2
Moderate	160	325	140	3
	170	350	160	4
Moderately hot	190	375	170	5
	200	400	180	6
Hot	220	425	200	7
	230	450	210	8
Very hot	240	475	220	9

Liquid measurements

Metric	Imperial	Australian	US
25ml	1fl oz		
60ml	2fl oz	$1/4$ cup	$1/4$ cup
75ml	3fl oz		
100ml	$3\frac{1}{2}$fl oz		
120ml	4fl oz	$1/2$ cup	$1/2$ cup
150ml	5fl oz		
180ml	6fl oz	$3/4$ cup	$3/4$ cup
200ml	7fl oz		
250ml	9fl oz	1 cup	1 cup
300ml	$10\frac{1}{2}$fl oz	$1\frac{1}{4}$ cups	$1\frac{1}{4}$ cups
350ml	$12\frac{1}{2}$fl oz	$1\frac{1}{2}$ cups	$1\frac{1}{2}$ cups
400ml	14fl oz	$1\frac{3}{4}$ cups	$1\frac{3}{4}$ cups
450ml	16fl oz	2 cups	2 cups
600ml	1 pint	$2\frac{1}{2}$ cups	$2\frac{1}{2}$ cups
750ml	$1\frac{1}{4}$ pints	3 cups	3 cups
900ml	$1\frac{1}{2}$ pints	$3\frac{1}{2}$ cups	$3\frac{1}{2}$ cups
1 litre	$1\frac{3}{4}$ pints	1 quart or 4 cups	1 quart or 4 cups
1.2 litres	2 pints		
1.4 litres	$2\frac{1}{2}$ pints		
1.5 litres	$2\frac{3}{4}$ pints		
1.7 litres	3 pints		
2 litres	$3\frac{1}{2}$ pints		

essential extras

Here's my list of suggested 50–150 calorie foods that you can use to supplement the 123 Plan. All calories listed in this list are approximate; a few wayward calories here and there won't make a difference to your allowance. See page 6 for more information on essential extras and how they fit into the plan. I've also listed some 'free' vegetable ideas, of which you can eat as much as you like! Make sure your plate is half filled with vegetables or salad, or serve them in a large bowl on the side. Eating more greens will help fill you up and provide lots of extra nutrients in your diet. Your skin will look better and the weight should drop off.

50 CALORIES PER SERVING

30g (about 5) ready-to-eat dried apricots
15g (1 tbsp) light mayo
30g (2 tbsp) hummus
40g drained artichoke antipasti in oil
60g whole olives

4 fresh apricots
200g fresh blackberries
200g fresh blackcurrants
100g fresh cherries
2 clementines or satsumas
100g fresh figs
½ grapefruit
85g grapes
2 kiwis
100g fresh mango
200g melon
1 medium nectarine
1 medium orange
1 medium peach
1 medium pear
125g fresh pineapple
100g canned pineapple in juice
2 plums
200g papaya
100g pomegranate seeds
200g raspberries
200g strawberries

100g fresh tomato salsa
50g tzatziki
1 level tbsp orange marmalade
1 level tbsp mango chutney
1 level tsp taramasalata
1 level tbsp honey

2cm slice (about 20g) ciabatta
1 x 10g rye crispbread, such as Ryvita
50g cooked puy lentils, green lentils
1 x measure (25ml) spirits (light or dark, e.g. rum, vodka)

1 tbsp single cream
1 tbsp half-fat crème fraiche
10g Parmesan
30g soft French goat's cheese
25g (1½ tbsp) light soft cheese
150ml orange juice (not from concentrate)
100ml regular soy milk
100g low-fat natural yoghurt
50g (about 3 wafer thin slices) of ham, turkey or chicken

75 CALORIES PER SERVING

150ml semi-skimmed milk
100g low-fat cottage cheese
25g (small wedge) Camembert
1 tbsp double cream
1 tbsp crème fraiche (full fat)
50g ricotta cheese
¼ 125g ball of fresh mozzarella

¼ average avocado (35g)
50g smoked salmon
1 rasher back bacon, grilled or dry-fried
50g cooked, skinless chicken breast
100g cooked jumbo prawns (about 9)

1 medium apple
100g blueberries
25g dried mango

2 cream crackers
20g rice cakes (2 or 3)
20g plain breadsticks (about 4)
½ English muffin
1 slice medium white or brown bread
15g shop-bought (not takeaway) prawn crackers
1 oatcake

½ 160g tin tuna in brine, drained
40g sun-dried (or sun-blush) tomatoes in oil, drained
30g (2 tbsp) raisins
1 medium egg, boiled

100 CALORIES PER SERVING

1 large egg
40g feta cheese
100g plain cottage cheese
50g (2½ tbsp) soured cream
25g blue cheese
100ml fresh custard
25g cooking chorizo
30g ready-to-eat chorizo
    (about 5 thin slices)
25g salami (about 5 thin
    slices)
1 heaped tbsp pesto

45g Parma ham
    (about 3 slices)
30g smoked mackerel fillet
1 medium banana

1 level tbsp peanut butter
1 tbsp extra virgin olive oil
30g popping corn kernels
20g unsalted plain cashews
20g tortilla chips
25g wasabi peas

20g plain crisps

1 slice of thick cut bread
½ plain bagel
1 x 45g soft white bread roll
½ regular pitta bread
1 slice German style rye bread
1 crumpet
120g baked beans
45g dried couscous
30g dried wholewheat pasta
25g dried soba noodles
30g dried quinoa

125ml wine (white, red, rose)
125ml sparkling wine/
    Champagne
½ pint lager
½ pint bitter
½ pint dry cider

150 CALORIES PER SERVING

35g Cheddar cheese
100g skinless chicken breast,
    baked or grilled

100g cooked brown rice
115g cooked easy-cook
    white rice
40g dried basmati rice
1 potato, baked, boiled
    or mashed without fat
    (195g raw weight)
130g baked sweet potato
    (about ½ large potato)
40g dried rice noodles
50g dried egg noodles
100g cooked pasta
40g porridge oats
50g shop-bought naan bread
    (about ½)

25g unsalted almonds
175ml wine (not sparkling)

'FREE' SAUCES

Brown sauce, in moderation;
    each tbsp is 24 calories
Fish sauce (nam pla)
Ketchup, in moderation;
    each tbsp is 20 calories
Horseradish sauce
Hot sauce (Tabasco)
Mint sauce (not jelly)
Mustard, any variety
    (English, Dijon,
    wholegrain, American)
Soy sauce
Vinegars (balsamic,
    white wine, malt, etc.)
Worcestershire sauce

Any herbs or spices

'FREE' VEGETABLES

Artichokes, including tinned
    hearts (but not in oil)
Asparagus
Aubergine
Baby sweetcorn
Beans, any green (not baked)
    (French, runner, etc.)
Bean sprouts
Beetroot, fresh, cooked
    or pickled
Broccoli
Brussels sprouts
Butternut squash
Cabbage, all kinds
    (Savoy, red, white)
Carrots
Cauliflower
Celeriac
Celery
Chicory
Chillies, including pickled
    jalapeños
Cornichons
Courgettes
Cucumber
Fennel
Garlic
Kale
Leeks
Lemons
Limes
Lettuce and salad greens
    (watercress, baby
    spinach, romaine)
Mangetout
Marrow
Mushrooms
Onions
Peppers
Pickled onions
Radishes
Shallots
Spring onions
Sugar snap peas
Swede
Tomatoes, including tinned
    (but not sun-dried)
Turnips

nutritional information
per serving

page 10 / serves 4
quick cheesy chicken and ham

353 energy (kcal)
1491 energy (kJ)
51.9 protein (g)
22.9 carbohydrate (g)
6.6 fat (g)
2.4 saturated fat (g)
3.6 fibre (g)
1.9 sugars (g)

page 12 / serves 4
soda can roast chicken with chipotle mayo

539/461* energy (kcal)
2259/1935* energy (kJ)
39.1/43.1* protein (g)
37 / 37 *carbohydrate (g)
27.1/16.5* fat (g)
7.2/3.8* saturated fat (g)
3.6/3.6* fibre* (g)
2.7/2.7* sugars* (g)
*without skin

page 14 / serves 4
all-in-one roast chicken dinner

463 energy (kcal)
1952 energy (kJ)
46.9 protein (g)
49.6 carbohydrate (g)
8.9 fat (g)
2.5 saturated fat (g)
11.9 fibre (g)
16.7 sugars (g)

page 16 / serves 4
barbecue-style chicken with wedges and corn

381 energy (kcal)
1609 energy (kJ)
40.3 protein (g)
37.8 carbohydrate (g)
8.7 fat (g)
2.8 saturated fat (g)
3.4 fibre (g)
10.1 sugars (g)

page 18 / serves 4
lemony chicken tray bake

361 energy (kcal)
1525 energy (kJ)
41 protein (g)
37.5 carbohydrate (g)
6.3 fat (g)
1.6 saturated fat (g)
7.5 fibre (g)
14.6 sugars (g)

page 20 / serves 6
no-fuss roast lamb

556 energy (kcal)
2332 energy (kJ)
47.5 protein (g)
45.9 carbohydrate (g)
20.2 fat (g)
6.9 saturated fat (g)
11.7 fibre (g)
14.5 sugars (g)

page 22 / serves 2
lamb with spring vegetables and mint

308 energy (kcal)
1294 energy (kJ)
22.8 protein (g)
35.5 carbohydrate (g)
9.1 fat (g)
3.5 saturated fat (g)
5.3 fibre (g)
12.7 sugars (g)

page 24 / serves 4
soy and ginger salmon with noodles

355 energy (kcal)
1491 energy (kJ)
31.2 protein (g)
24.6 carbohydrate (g)
14.9 fat (g)
2.4 saturated fat (g)
4.2 fibre (g)
14 sugars (g)

page 26 / serves 2
warm tuna niçoise

430/107* energy (kcal)
1809/442* energy (kJ)
34.5/0.2* protein (g)
41.8/1.2* carbohydrate (g)
14.9 fat/11.2* (g)
2.91.6* saturated fat (g)
7.4/0.2* fibre (g)
11.4/1.2* sugars (g)
*vinaigrette

page 28 / serves 2
one-pan cooked breakfast

293 energy (kcal)
1218 energy (kJ)
20.7 protein (g)
7.3 carbohydrate (g)
20.2 fat (g)
7.6 saturated fat (g)
1.9 fibre (g)
3.4 sugars (g)

page 30 / serves 6
easy apple and blackberry fruit pie

339 energy (kcal)
1421 energy (kJ)
4.2 protein (g)
41.9 carbohydrate (g)
18.4 fat (g)
5.6 saturated fat (g)
4 fibre (g)
12 sugars (g)

page 34 / serves 4
chilli chicken stir-fry with rice

305 energy (kcal)
1288 energy (kJ)
31.3 protein (g)
35 carbohydrate (g)
5.3 fat (g)
1 saturated fat (g)
3.7 fibre (g)
8.8 sugars (g)

page 36 / serves 4
chicken and ham wok lasagne

467 energy (kcal)
1966 energy (kJ)
56.1 protein (g)
30.4 carbohydrate (g)
11.8 fat (g)
6 saturated fat (g)
2.3 fibre (g)
6.8 sugars (g)

page 38 / serves 4
coconut chicken curry

429 energy (kcal)
1799 energy (kJ)
40.1 protein (g)
29.7 carbohydrate (g)
17.3 fat (g)
7.6 saturated fat (g)
5.1 fibre (g)
9.3 sugars (g)

page 40 / serves 4
hoisin meatball stir-fry

286 energy (kcal)
1195 energy (kJ)
21.3 protein (g)
23.9 carbohydrate (g)
11.9 fat (g)
4.9 saturated fat (g)
5.1 fibre (g)
11.2 sugars (g)

page 42 / serves 4
creamy pork, apples and cabbage

346 energy (kcal)
1459 energy (kJ)
32.1 protein (g)
29.2 carbohydrate (g)
10.6 fat (g)
3.4 saturated fat (g)
7.6 fibre (g)
13.3 sugars (g)

page 44 / serves 2
ginger and chilli prawn wraps

162 energy (kcal)
683 energy (kJ)
19.7 protein (g)
18 carbohydrate (g)
1.6 fat (g)
0.3 saturated fat (g)
4.2 fibre (g)
9.8 sugars (g)

page 46 / serves 4
goan fish curry

286 energy (kcal)
1195 energy (kJ)
25.8 protein (g)
13.3 carbohydrate (g)
14.5 fat (g)
9.4 saturated fat (g)
3.5 fibre (g)
9.4 sugars (g)

page 48 / serves 4
paneer and vegetable curry

367 energy (kcal)
1534 energy (kJ)
19.1 protein (g)
31.5 carbohydrate (g)
18.9 fat (g)
10.8 saturated fat (g)
6.5 fibre (g)
10.2 sugars (g)

page 50 / serves 4
vegetable pakoras

277/25* energy (kcal)
1141/106* energy (kJ)
6.8/2.4* protein (g)
26.5/3.8* carbohydrate (g)
14.7/0.1* fat (g)
1.7/0* saturated fat (g)
6.4/0.3* fibre (g)
3.8/3.4* sugars (g)
*minted cucumber yoghurt

page 54 / serves 6
leek and potato soup

140 energy (kcal)
586 energy (kJ)
4 protein (g)
21.3 carbohydrate (g)
4.8 fat (g)
1.8 saturated fat (g)
4.6 fibre (g)
5.7 sugars (g)

page 56 / serves 6
carrot, sweet potato and coriander soup

108 energy (kcal)
455 energy (kJ)
1.8 protein (g)
21.3 carbohydrate (g)
2.4 fat (g)
0.4 saturated fat (g)
5.2 fibre (g)
11.9 sugars (g)

page 58 / serves 5
hob-top chicken biryani

356 energy (kcal)
1487 energy (kJ)
28.2 protein (g)
38.1 carbohydrate (g)
10.2 fat (g)
1.7 saturated fat (g)
6.1 fibre (g)
9.4 sugars (g)

page 60 / serves 4
harissa chicken and bulgur pilaf

328 energy (kcal)
1373 energy (kJ)
27.1 protein (g)
37.9 carbohydrate (g)
8 fat (g)
1.2 saturated fat (g)
3 fibre (g)
1.2 sugars (g)

page 62 / serves 4
simple sausage stew

394 energy (kcal)
1645 energy (kJ)
23.8 protein (g)
23.8 carbohydrate (g)
20.3 fat (g)
6.6 saturated fat (g)
5.1 fibre (g)
12.4 sugars (g)

page 64 / serves 5
bolognese pasta pot

414 energy (kcal)
1744 energy (kJ)
45.7 protein (g)
45.7 carbohydrate (g)
10.6 fat (g)
4.4 saturated fat (g)
2.4 fibre (g)
5.9 sugars (g)

page 66 / serves 4
italian fish stew

365 energy (kcal)
1538 energy (kJ)
27.6 protein (g)
43.9 carbohydrate (g)
6.7 fat (g)
1 saturated fat (g)
4.1 fibre (g)
8.9 sugars (g)

page 68 / serves 6
caponata with cannellini beans

134/378* energy (kcal)
565/1599* energy (kJ)
23.9/14.7* protein (g)
23.9/69.4* carbohydrate (g)
2.4/6.6* fat (g)
0.2/0.8* saturated fat (g)
4.3/7.2* fibre (g)
16.2/18.9* sugars (g)
*caponata on toast

page 70 / serves 4
coconut and sweet potato dhal

378 energy (kcal)
1596 energy (kJ)
61 protein (g)
61 carbohydrate (g)
10 fat (g)
6.1 saturated fat (g)
9.1 fibre (g)
12.2 sugars (g)

page 72 / serves 6
fruity tapicoa puddings

142 energy (kcal)
604 energy (kJ)
28.9 protein (g)
28.9 carbohydrate (g)
1.9 fat (g)
1.2 saturated fat (g)
1.1 fibre (g)
13.1 sugars (g)

page 74 / serves 8
lower-fat vanilla ice cream

130 energy (kcal)
543 energy (kj)
4.7 protein (g)
8.9 carbohydrate (g)
8.7 fat (g)
4.1 saturated fat (g)
0 fibre (g)
8.0 sugars (g)

page 78 / serves 4
chicken and vegetable frying pan pie

377 energy (kcal)
1569 energy (kJ)
32.4 protein (g)
35.3 carbohydrate (g)
10.7 fat (g)
4.5 saturated fat (g)
4.9 fibre (g)
7.7 sugars (g)

page 80 / serves 2
italian chicken with mascarpone

351 energy (kcal)
1474 energy (kJ)
40.7 protein (g)
14.1 carbohydrate (g)
12.5 fat (g)
4.2 saturated fat (g)
2.4 fibre (g)
11.9 sugars (g)

page 82 / serves 2
pan-fried pesto chicken

329 energy (kcal)
1383 energy (kJ)
43.1 protein (g)
18.5 carbohydrate (g)
18.5 fat (g)
15.5 saturated fat (g)
3.8 fibre (g)
15.5 sugars (g)

page 85 / serves 2
smoky steak fajitas

483 energy (kcal)
2035 energy (kJ)
34.9 protein (g)
49.3 carbohydrate (g)
17.6 fat (g)
6.9 saturated fat (g)
6 fibre (g)
11.4 sugars (g)

page 86 / serves 5
tortilla chilli pie

352 energy (kcal)
1476 energy (kJ)
31 protein (g)
21.7 carbohydrate (g)
14 fat (g)
5.7 saturated fat (g)
6.8 fibre (g)
7.8 sugars (g)

page 88 / serves 2
moussaka for two

496 energy (kcal)
2065 energy (kJ)
30.6 protein (g)
14.9 carbohydrate (g)
33.5 fat (g)
17.8 saturated fat (g)
5.9 fibre (g)
10.7 sugars (g)

page 90 / serves 2
salmon with puy lentils

498 energy (kcal)
2083 energy (kJ)
37.6 protein (g)
34.7 carbohydrate (g)
21.7 fat (g)
3.4 saturated fat (g)
11.2 fibre (g)
9.8 sugars (g)

page 92 / serves 3
spanish omelette

371 energy (kcal)
1550 energy (kJ)
20.9 protein (g)
25.7 carbohydrate (g)
21.1 fat (g)
5.9 saturated fat (g)
4.5 fibre (g)
9.4 sugars (g)

page 94 / serves 2
warm griddled halloumi salad

499 energy (kcal)
2074 energy (kJ)
28.5 protein (g)
16.7 carbohydrate (g)
35.7 fat (g)
20.4 saturated fat (g)
5.4 fibre (g)
14.1 sugars (g)

page 96 / serves 4
caribbean pineapple

120/56* energy (kcal)
507/240* energy (kJ)
0.6/1.5* protein (g)
20.2/13* carb (g)
4.8/0.2* fat (g)
2.1/0.1* saturated fat (g)
2/0.7* fibre (g)
20.2/11.8* sugars (g)
*banana 'ice cream'

page 100 / serves 4
baked chicken and mushroom risotto

420 energy (kcal)
1772 energy (kJ)
37.2 protein (g)
47.2 carbohydrate (g)
6.2 fat (g)
2.9 saturated fat (g)
2 fibre (g)
5.4 sugars (g)

page 102 / serves 2
couscous with roasted roots, honey and goat's cheese

416 energy (kcal)
1751 energy (kJ)
12.4 protein (g)
66.9 carbohydrate (g)
11.6 fat (g)
3.9 saturated fat (g)
16.1 fibre (g)
26.6 sugars (g)

page 104 / serves 4
spiced lamb-stuffed courgettes

273 energy (kcal)
1137 energy (kJ)
17.3 protein (g)
24.7 carbohydrate (g)
11.8 fat (g)
3.7 saturated fat (g)
1.9 fibre (g)
6.4 sugars (g)

page 106 / serves 4
salmon and asparagus crustless quiche

254 energy (kcal)
1058 energy (kJ)
16.2 protein (g)
8.4 carbohydrate (g)
17.5 fat (g)
7.4 saturated fat (g)
1.6 fibre (g)
3.0 sugars (g)

page 108 / serves 2
spanish baked fish with chorizo

416 energy (kcal)
1747 energy (kJ)
42.5 protein (g)
30.6 carbohydrate (g)
14.5 fat (g)
3.7 saturated fat (g)
12.4 fibre (g)
14.3 sugars (g)

page 110 / makes 6
chinese rice-stuffed peppers

104 energy (kcal)
439 energy (kJ)
4.7 protein (g)
17.1 carbohydrate (g)
2.3 fat (g)
0.6 saturated fat (g)
3.9 fibre (g)
8.3 sugars (g)

page 112 / serves 4
easy baked apples

208 energy (kcal)
873 energy (kJ)
2.1 protein (g)
33.3 carbohydrate (g)
8.2 fat (g)
3.5 saturated fat (g)
3.8 fibre (g)
32.9 sugars (g)

page 114 / serves 6
nectarine and blueberry muffin cobbler

251 energy (kcal)
1056 energy (kJ)
6.1 protein (g)
36.9 carbohydrate (g)
9.6 fat (g)
5.1 saturated fat (g)
2.1 fibre (g)
17.4 sugars (g)

page 116 / serves 12
quick-mix banana and sultana cake

173 energy (kcal)
727 energy (kJ)
4.1 protein (g)
25.7 carbohydrate (g)
6.7 fat (g)
1.1 saturated fat (g)
1.3 fibre (g)
9.7 sugars (g)

page 120 / serves 4
tarragon chicken

321 energy (kcal)
1342 energy (kJ)
28.2 protein (g)
19.7 carbohydrate (g)
13 fat (g)
7 saturated fat (g)
5.1 fibre (g)
7.6 sugars (g)

page 122 / serves 5
simple cassoulet

480 energy (kcal)
2008 energy (kJ)
42.7 protein (g)
28.6 carbohydrate (g)
20 fat (g)
6.8 saturated fat (g)
7.7 fibre (g)
10.7 sugars (g)

page 124 / serves 5
oven-baked chicken and prawn paella

445 energy (kcal)
1875 energy (kJ)
40.3 protein (g)
45.7 carbohydrate (g)
8.9 fat (g)
3 saturated fat (g)
2.3 fibre (g)
5.2 sugars (g)

page 126 / serves 6
all-in-one beef and ale stew

382 energy (kcal)
1606 energy (kJ)
32.1 protein (g)
39.2 carbohydrate (g)
10.2 fat (g)
3.4 saturated fat (g)
8.6 fibre (g)
15.7 sugars (g)

page 128 / serves 5
chinese braised beef with noodles

430 energy (kcal)
1812 energy (kJ)
43.7 protein (g)
33.9 carbohydrate (g)
13.3 fat (g)
4.7 saturated fat (g)
4.7 fibre (g)
14.5 sugars (g)

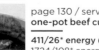

page 130 / serves 6
one-pot beef curry

411/26* energy (kcal)
1724/108* energy (kJ)
44.7/2.1* protein (g)
25.5/4.3* carbohydrate (g)
15/0.1* fat (g)
4.9/0 saturated fat (g)
5.7/0.3 fibre (g)
11.7/4.2 sugars (g)
*minted cucumber raita

page 132 / serves 6
pibil pulled pork tacos

432/13* energy (kcal)
1803/53* energy (kJ)
34.5/0.3* protein (g)
18.2/2.7* carbohydrate (g)
24.2/0* fat (g)
6.2/0* saturated fat (g)
1.9/0.5* fibre (g)
2.4/2.1* sugars (g)
*pickled red onion

page 134 / serves 6
moroccan lamb tagine

415 energy (kcal)
1737 energy (kJ)
30 protein (g)
29.6 carbohydrate (g)
20.4 fat (g)
8.4 saturated fat (g)
6 fibre (g)
13.5 sugars (g)

page 136 / serves 4
one-pan fish pie

305 energy (kcal)
1285 energy (kJ)
29.2 protein (g)
22 carbohydrate (g)
11.8 fat (g)
6 saturated fat (g)
3.2 fibre (g)
7.4 sugars (g)

page 138 / serves 5
mulled pears

90 energy (kcal)
384 energy (kJ)
0.4 protein (g)
19 carbohydrate (g)
1 fat (g)
0 saturated fat (g)
1.5 fibre (g)
17.8 sugars (g)

page 142 / serves 6
chicken, quinoa, avocado and chilli salad

324 energy (kcal)
1360 energy (kJ)
27.8 protein (g)
23.2 carbohydrate (g)
13.9 fat (g)
3 saturated fat (g)
5.1 fibre (g)
4.7 sugars (g)

page 144 / serves 2
satay chicken wraps

359 energy (kcal)
1504 energy (kJ)
37.8 protein (g)
18.8 carbohydrate (g)
15.2 fat (g)
3.8 saturated fat (g)
5.4 fibre (g)
13 sugars (g)

page 146 / serves 2
avocado on toast

277 energy (kcal)
1159 energy (kJ)
7.1 protein (g)
28.7 carbohydrate (g)
15.6 fat (g)
3.2 saturated fat (g)
7.5 fibre (g)
3.9 sugars (g)

page 148 / serves 2
nectarine, prosciutto and mozzarella salad

362 energy (kcal)
1512 energy (kJ)
23.6 protein (g)
16.2 carbohydrate (g)
22.9 fat (g)
10.9 saturated fat (g)
2.8 fibre (g)
16 sugars (g)

page 150 / serves 4
giant prawn cocktail

176 energy (kcal)
738 energy (kJ)
22.2 protein (g)
9.3 carbohydrate (g)
5.7 fat (g)
1 saturated fat (g)
2.7 fibre (g)
8.5 sugars (g)

page 152 / serves 2
yoghurt with banana and dates

225/135* energy (kcal)
974/576* energy (kJ)
18.4/9.4* protein (g)
32.4/24.2* carbohydrate (g)
3.7/0.6* fat (g)
0.6/0.2* saturated fat (g)
2.4/2.4* fibre (g)
30.1/22.8* sugars (g)
*berry yoghurt

page 154 / serves 8
apple, melon, pineapple and pomegranate salad

60 energy (kcal)
258 energy (kJ)
1 protein (g)
14.5 carbohydrate (g)
0.2 fat (g)
0 saturated fat (g)
3 fibre (g)
14.5 sugars (g)

page 156 / serves 5
mango, grape and apple salad

98 energy (kcal)
418 energy (kJ)
1 protein (g)
24.6 carbohydrate (g)
0.2 fat (g)
0 saturated fat (g)
3.5 fibre (g)
24.5 sugars (g)

page 160 / serves 6
smoked salmon breakfast muffins

107 energy (kcal)
446 energy (kJ)
9.5 protein (g)
0.2 carbohydrate (g)
7.6 fat (g)
2.3 saturated fat (g)
0.1 fibre (g)
0.2 sugars (g)

page 162 / serves 6
smoked mackerel pâté

156 energy (kcal)
645 energy (kJ)
10.1 protein (g)
2.4 carbohydrate (g)
11.7 fat (g)
2.3 saturated fat (g)
0.1 fibre (g)
2 sugars (g)

page 164 / serves 2
tuna and bean layered salad pots

433 energy (kcal)
1806 energy (kJ)
27 protein (g)
28.5 carb (g)
24 fat (g)
3.5 saturated fat (g)
8 fibre (g)
11.2 sugars (g)

page 166 / serves 4
swirly lemon yoghurt pots

92 energy (kcal)
405 energy (kJ)
10.7 protein (g)
12.2 carbohydrate (g)
0.6 fat (g)
0.2 saturated fat (g)
0.8 fibre (g)
9.7 sugars (g)

page 168 / serves 4
milk chocolate pots

176 energy (kcal)
742 energy (kJ)
8.9 protein (g)
20.5 carbohydrate (g)
7.1 fat (g)
4.3 saturated fat (g)
0.8 fibre (g)
20.1 sugars (g)

page 170 / serves 4
banoffee yoghurt pots

187 energy (kcal)
805 energy (kJ)
11.7 protein (g)
31.4 carbohydrate (g)
2.8 fat (g)
1.4 saturated fat (g)
0.7 fibre (g)
24.9 sugars (g)

page 172 / serves 4
summer berry crunch pies

203 energy (kcal)
855 energy (kJ)
3.2 protein (g)
37.1 carbohydrate (g)
5.6 fat (g)
3.4 saturated fat (g)
4 fibre (g)
16.1 sugars (g)

page 174 / serves 4
strawberry, blackcurrant and banana smoothie

159 energy (kcal)
672 energy (kJ)
6.7 protein (g)
30.2 carbohydrate (g)
1.9 fat (g)
0.8 saturated fat (g)
2.6 fibre (g)
25.6 sugars (g)

index

First published in Great Britain in 2016
by Orion Publishing Group Ltd
Carmelite House, 50 Victoria Embankment
London, EC4Y 0DZ
An Hachette UK Company

10 9 8 7 6 5 4 3 2 1

A CIP catalogue record for this book is available
from the British Library.
ISBN: 978 1 4091 5479 2

Designer: Smith & Gilmour
Photographer: Cristian Barnett
Props stylist: Claire Bignell
Creative director: Justine Pattison
Nutritional analysis calculated by: Lauren Brignell
Recipe assistants: Rebecca Roberts, Gileng Salter
Kitchen assistants: Jess Blain, Emily PB, Hasmita Gohil
Project editor: Jillian Young
Copy editor: Laura Nickoll
Proofreader: Mary-Jane Wilkins
Indexer: Rosemary Dear

Printed and bound in China

*Every effort has been made to ensure that the
information in this book is accurate. The information
will be relevant to the majority of people but may not
be applicable in each individual case, so it is advised
that professional medical advice is obtained for
specific health matters. Neither the publisher nor
author accept any legal responsibility for any personal
injury or other damage or loss arising from the use or
misuse of the information in this book. Anyone making
a change in their diet should consult their GP,
especially if pregnant, infirm, elderly or under 16.*

The Orion Publishing Group's policy is to use papers
that are natural, renewable and recyclable products
and made from wood grown in sustainable forests.
The logging and manufacturing processes are
expected to conform to the environmental
regulations of the country of origin.

www.orionbooks.co.uk

Acknowledgements

Firstly, huge thanks to everyone who enjoys my recipes
and the way I cook. You have given me such fantastic
feedback; I hope you like these dishes just as much.

An enormous thank you to John, Jess and Emily for
tasting and appraising over 500 new recipes in the
past 18 months!

I'm truly grateful to the very talented photographer
Cristian Barnett for wonderful photographs that
really make my food come to life. And the brilliant
Claire Bignell for her superb creative skills, selecting
the perfect props and helping make the recipes look
both beautiful and achievable. Massive thanks to
Lauren Brignell for all her invaluable nutritional support
and the hundreds of recipes she has analysed over the
past few months. Also, thanks to Rebecca Roberts for
carefully testing recipes and assisting on shoot days.
Not forgetting Annabel Wray, Annie Simpson and
Charlotte Page for their hard work in the test kitchen.

At Orion, I would like to thank Amanda Harris for
believing in this project right from the beginning
and for trusting me to get on and develop the series.
Also thank you to Jillian Young, my fantastic editor,
for her guidance and professionalism and Helen Ewing
for her design support.

A big thank you to everyone at Smith & Gilmour for
making the books look eye-catching, practical and
readable. I'm also grateful to my agent, Zoe King, at
The Blair Partnership, for her constant encouragement
and enthusiasm.

And a final heartfelt thank you to my family and my
friends for their fantastic support.